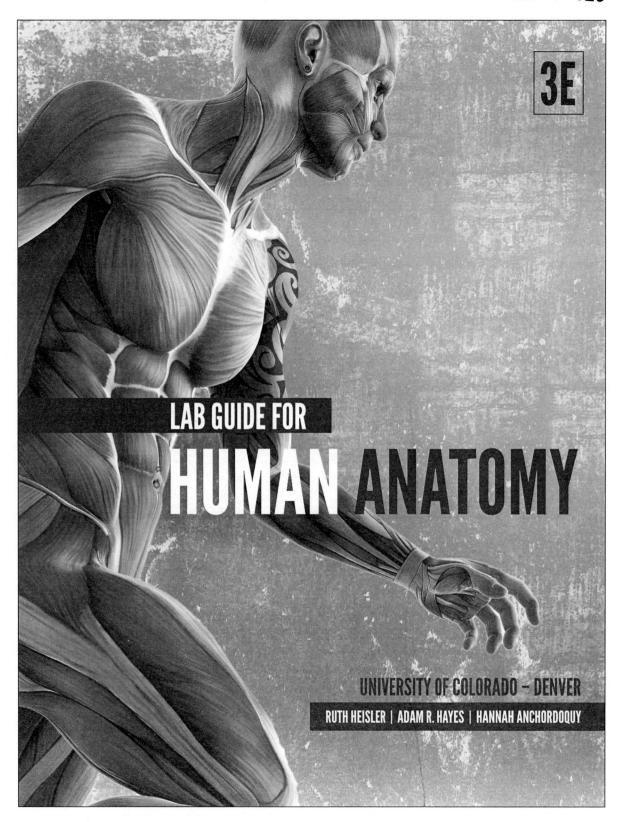

3E

LAB GUIDE FOR
HUMAN ANATOMY

UNIVERSITY OF COLORADO – DENVER

RUTH HEISLER | ADAM R. HAYES | HANNAH ANCHORDOQUY

bluedoor
flexible & affordable learning solutions™

Chief Executive Officer: Jon K. Earl

President, College: Lucas Tomasso
President, Private Sector: Dawn Earl
Director of Operations and Strategy: Michael Schafer

Print Solutions Manager: Connie Dayton
Digital Solutions Manager: Amber Wahl
Developmental & Production Coordinator: Rhiannon Nelson
Senior Project Coordinator: Dan Woods
Senior Project Coordinator: Peggy Li
Project Coordinator: Erica Rieck
Project Coordinator: Jessie Steigauf
Project Coordinator: Nicole Tupy
Production Assistant: Stephanie Larson

Cover Design: Dan Woods

ISBN-13: 978-1-59984-888-4

© 2015 by Ruth Heisler, Adam R. Hayes, Hannah Anchordoquy, and bluedoor, LLC.

© Cover images by Shutterstock.

Published by bluedoor, LLC
    10949 Bren Road East
    Minneapolis, MN 55343-9613
    800-979-1624
    www.bluedoorpublishing.com

Printed in the United States of America.
10 9 8 7 6 5 4 3 2 1

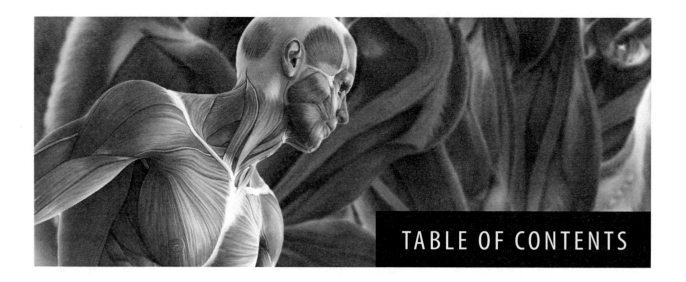

TABLE OF CONTENTS

ACKNOWLEDGMENTS

Many individuals over many years contributed to shaping the pedagogy and content of this manual. Ann Repka, Cliff Barnes, and Leif Saul at the University of Colorado, Boulder, were particularly influential. Further, the input from Teaching Assistants has been invaluable in the quest to continually improve this resource. My deep thanks to all of them.

INTRODUCTION

PREFACE

This laboratory guide has been written to assist the Human Anatomy student with the question: "What do I need to know for this course?" The text and atlas contain many detailed diagrams rich with anatomical structures. For each body system you will not be required to learn every structure on every figure. This guide provides a list of the structures you will be required to know for the lab portion of this course. However, this is more than just a list of structures to be identified in the lab. For some organ systems, short descriptions or background information precedes a section. These are included to give you a framework in which to understand the anatomy. You will also find questions to be answered and tables to be completed. Be sure you answer the questions, and have completed the tables, as lab practical exam questions may be taken from this material. Make sure you have seen all structures on the cadaver, models, charts or diagrams, figures, and microscopic slides.

Anatomy and anatomical terms are often confusing to the beginning student. It is only by preparing ahead that you can begin to understand the material to be covered. In order to make the best use of your time in the laboratory, and to enhance your learning experience, **it is highly recommended that you prepare ahead of time using the following guidelines:**

1. Read any indicated pages in the text prior to coming to lab.

2. Highlight the structures identified in this guide on the figures and diagrams in your atlas and text (this will enable you to filter out additional information contained in your atlas and text for which you are not responsible for lab).

3. Review the structures in your atlas and corresponding diagrams **AND figures in your text** (this will help your performance in lecture, too!).

4. Fill in the tables and, with the help of your text book, answer the questions posed in the manual. DON'T USE LAB TIME TO FILL IN THE TABLES! You can answer the questions and fill in the tables any time.

5. USE THE TIME IN LAB TO LOOK AT THE SPECIMENS. You cannot take the models or cadavers home, so ensure that you are taking advantage of all the time you DO have with the cadavers, models, and bones.

6. If you find material confusing, or don't understand some terminology, jot down questions to ask your TA.

7. After lab is over, take some time to review what you've learned. It will help you retain the information.

8. Anatomy is a visual discipline, therefore, it is ***strongly*** encouraged that you try your hand at drawing and labeling structures from memory.

9. Teach it. Locate and name the structures, showing AND explaining them to anyone who will listen. Articulating the names of structures (without looking at figures!), describing them in your own words, and forcing yourself to organize the content to make it understandable to someone else is a powerful way of learning the material.

10. And if you haven't already done it, draw and label, draw and label, draw and label!!!

Time in lab is a very valuable resource. The structure and extended contact time with instructors will enable you to solicit many suggestions on how to learn and retain what seems to be an overwhelming amount of material. Use the instructors often, but please use them with care.

The study of the structure of the human body is fascinating. Your experience in lab will hopefully leave you amazed, enthralled, and hungry for more. Get in, get your "hands dirty" and have a wonderful time!

I. LABORATORY POLICIES, CONDUCT, AND SUPPLIES

The human anatomy laboratory uses a variety of materials, including models, preserved specimens, microscope slides, charts, human bones, and prosected human cadavers. The learning materials to which you will have access are often very breakable and expensive. Please take responsibility for the safe and respectful handling of lab materials. The experience with human cadavers serves as a valuable learning tool, and is one afforded to few people. It is expected that all students will show respect and dignity toward the cadavers. **If any student treats the cadavers with disrespect, defaces the cadavers in any way, or removes human anatomical specimens from the laboratory, a failing grade will be given for the course.**

1. You cannot attend a lab section other than the one you are registered for. If you need to switch a lab in an emergency, contact your instructor and Dr. A first.

2. **Eating or drinking in the laboratory is strictly forbidden at all times**.

3. Please treat the instructor, the teaching assistants, and your peers with respect. In particular, be aware that the TA's go WELL beyond what is expected of them, offering extra office hours and learning opportunities. Without exception, they are dedicated, hard-working students with a demonstrated work ethic, high moral character, gregarious nature, and an ability to communicate. Treat them with the respect that they are due.

4. Taking pictures in the lab violates class policy, university policy, and can result in State and Federal criminal charges.

5. **No visitors allowed in the lab allowed. There are no exceptions.**

6. The human bone specimens are valuable and delicate. Please use hands or pipe cleaners gently when working with these specimens and do not put pens, pencils, or probes in the foramen.

7. APPROPRIATE LAB ATTIRE IS MANDATORY. If you are not properly dressed, you will not be allowed in lab. THIS INCLUDES PRACTICALS. If you forget a required clothing article, you can certainly borrow, purchase, or go back home and retrieve the appropriate item, and then attend lab. Appropriate clothing includes:

    - Closed-toed shoes. Crocs are not OK. Mules are not OK. Ballet flats are not OK.

    - Pants, long skirts, and leggings are OK; Capri's, "man-crops", mini-skirts, shorts, and nylons are not.

    - A shirt that covers your shoulders. T-shirts are OK; tank tops and spaghetti straps are not, and tube tops are right out. Given the materials handled in lab you may WANT to always wear long sleeves.

    - Gloves on each hand are required whenever human remains are handled. Gloves will be provided in lab – you do not need to bring your own.

- Although some sort of protective clothing is desirable in lab, it is optional and does not need to be a lab coat. Often, students wear scrubs, and bring a change of clothes. An oversized flannel shirt from a second-hand store works as an inexpensive alternative. Having a sealable plastic bag in which to place your lab clothes will limit how much the rest of the contents of your backpack smell of anatomy lab.

- Hair ties are advised for students with long hair.

- Contact wearers may find the preservative irritates their eyes – you may want to bring your glasses with you just in case. Additionally, although it is not required that you wear them, safety glasses may alleviate eye irritation if you find it problematic.

8. **There is a lot of work to do for lab!!** THE LAB IS WHERE THE REAL LEARNING WILL OCCUR – BUT ONLY IF YOU DO THE NECESSARY PREPARATORY WORK BEFOREHAND! There are blank tables in the lab manual. All the terms that you need to know to complete these tables are in the lab chapter or the text. Don't use valuable lab time to fill in tables!!! Look up the material, answer the questions, and fill in the tables BEFORE lab so that you are able to make the best possible use of the limited time you do have in lab. In a course such as this, repetition is EXTREMELY important.

9. Lab practicals **will** require more than simple identification. We will be integrating information from lecture, as it is appropriate. As you learn things in lab, make sure that you know what they connect to, what they do, how they relate to other structures, what tissues form them. If you are not keeping up with the lecture material, you risk performing poorly in lab. Make sure that you spend the necessary time each week to keep up!

10. Each day in lab will entail a combination of activities. You can expect your TA to spend time at the beginning of lab relating the day's topic to the foundation material it reinforces. Then you will have time to explore the materials available in lab on your own or in a group, self-guided or with assistance from your TA.

11. Active participation in lab is essential to success in anatomy. You must handle the materials, say the names out loud, and practice, practice, practice. It is often helpful to work with a partner, quizzing each other and demonstrating structures to each other.

12. Filling in tables and studying the book is NOT effective use of the limited time you have in lab. COME TO LAB PREPARED. Know what you will be studying and look through the material in your book/atlas BEFORE you come to lab so you can use your lab time going over the specimens.

13. Please pay attention in lab to distribution of waste items. Your TA will instruct you in the proper receptacles for glove, paper, and tissue disposal.

14. **Please treat the cadavers with respect, and use them to the best of your ability. This is the best way you can honor their gift. Inappropriate treatment of the cadavers will not be tolerated and will result in your removal from the course.**

15. **You must be professional in your comments about lab and the cadavers.** Please remember that people around you, on AND off campus (on the train, the bus, in line) may have loved ones who have donated their bodies for education. Imagine how a comment from you regarding one of our cadavers might make them feel....

II. LAB SAFETY

In all lab activities, safety is paramount! Please, use common sense, realize we are working with sharp objects and chemical hazards. Understand that you are responsible for making mature, common-sense decisions. It is expected that spills and accidents will happen. BE RESPONSIBLE ABOUT DEALING WITH THEM – if you do not know what to do, identify the problem to your TA so you can make sure it is dealt with safely and properly. No one gets in trouble for having accidents – but not taking responsibility for dealing with them when they do happen is problematic!

1. When working with the cadavers or any animal tissue, it is **required** that you wear gloves.

2. Wearing a lab coat or oversized shirt is also recommended as a way to protect your clothes and yourself from odor and preservatives.

3. Contact wearers may experience eye discomfort. It is recommended that you wear glasses to lab, but if you insist on wearing contacts then chemistry goggles may alleviate discomfort.

4. Cadavers are fixed (preserved) using a solution including, formalin, phenol, methanol, glycerin, and water.

   • Formalin is a known carcinogen, but the concentration used is well within safety guidelines. However, some chemically sensitive individuals may experience itching, rashes, or respiratory problems. If you experience any of these problems, you can take the following steps to alleviate the problem:

      • wear chemistry type goggles to protect your eyes (this especially applies to contact wearers who would rather not wear their glasses)

      • be certain to cover all exposed skin (wear a lab coat) and do not touch anything without gloves

      • if you feel you would like a respirator that filters out formalin, contact the lab coordinator (hannah.anchordoquy@ucdenver.edu) for more information. Professional fitting through University Environmental Health and Safety is required, and costs about $100. Additionally, arranging the fit testing and securing a respirator tends to take several weeks, so please plan accordingly.

   • Please communicate with your TA regarding further suggestions if you continue to experience eye, skin, or respiratory irritation.

5. **Note:** If you are pregnant, I encourage you to consider delaying taking the course until after you have delivered your baby(ies). I strongly urge you to discuss this with your obstetrician, since some of these chemicals have been shown to be teratogenic in high concentrations. With that said, a number of pregnant women, in consultation with their obstetricians, have taken (and taught!) the course without problems.

III. LAB PRACTICALS

Your lab performance will be gauged, in part, using timed practicals. Practicals will be administered at various points throughout the semester. They are NOT comprehensive. **There are no make-up exams for missed lab practicals!** Please refer to the course syllabus for specifics regarding missed exams.

Format, Mechanics, and the Diction of a Typical Question:

- Upon entering the lab, students will leave all belongings including any electronics at the front of the room under the whiteboard. Students are only allowed to carry pens, pencils, and an eraser with them during the practical.

- TAs will provide a clipboard and answer form for completing the exam.

- Each lab practical consists of **20 stations** with **4 questions at each station**.

  - The first lab practical will not ask questions that utilize cadavers. All other practicals will be heavily weighted with cadaver questions.

  - Microscopes are used to ask questions from real body tissues. Students can expect to be asked questions from microscopes at up to three stations during any of the lab practicals.

- Students rotate sequentially through stations every 4 minutes. All students in a lab section begin and end at the same time.

- During the practical, students are encouraged to ask clarifying questions of their TA, but may not communicate with other students in any way.

- After rotating through all 20 stations, students are permitted an additional **4 minutes to check spelling and completeness** of the exam. Students are **not** permitted to return to any station during this time, and must stand at the station where they ended until time is called, after which they turn their answer sheet into their TA.

  - Example:

    - Section L01: Alejandro begins at station #1 and ends after station #20. 7:05 am-8:29 am. Lana begins at station #15 and ends after station #14. 7:05 am-8:29 am.

- Question terminology you can expect:

  - Care is taken when writing the practicals to be as clear as possible regarding what structure you are to identify. To that end, you will encounter helpful terminology.

  - "Name feature A". "Name structure B". This type of terminology is intended to guide you to anatomical landmarks that project, such as a process or a condyle. These landmarks may be on many different scales, such as an entire organ, a tuberosity, a layer of the epidermis, an osteon, or the axon of a neuron.

  - "Name space D". "Name depression E". Sometimes we will use terms such as "groove", "depression", or "hole" to indicate anatomical features that are recessed, rather than projected. Examples include a sinus, foramen, fossa, or a body cavity. Similarly, "tube" may be used to indicate hollow structures not filled with blood or lymph, such as ducts or a section of the intestines.

  - "Name vessel H". "Name nerve I". "Name tendon J". Usually (though not always!), if the name of an artery or vein is requested, the question will ask you to name the vessel. Similarly, if the name of a nerve is requested, the question will you to name the nerve, and if the name of a muscle is requested, the question will ask you to name the muscle. However, there WILL be occasions when we assess whether you can identify the type of structure labeled. So, you will need to be able to differentiate a nerve from a muscle, artery, vein, ligament, tendon, etc.

- "Name bone K". In this instance, name the bone, not any of the bone features or spaces. Often the question will ask you to name a specific feature AND the bone.

- Often, though not always, question terminology such as "be specific" is included in a question to remind you to provide the most detailed answer possible.

Note: Pay attention to the questions! Understanding the level of detail the question requests is a key component to laboratory practicals. Frequently we are seeking the most specific answer possible in relation to the terms being tested from the lab manual. Although the phrase "be specific" may be used to remind you to include as much detail as possible, at other times, the level of specificity sought is implied by the location and placement of the pin or pipe cleaner. Always consider the context of the unit being tested. Ultimately, if at any time you are confused or unsure about what a question is asking, please raise your hand and have your TA clarify the level of detail the answer requires. While your TA can more clearly indicate the structure, space, or item the question is focused on, they will not review your current answer or give clues or hints in any form.

IV. GRADING POLICIES

- **Anything** in the lab guide is fair game for practical testing. *This includes information from the tables and explicit questions within the guide that students are expected to complete outside of the lab. Please be aware that useful information regarding what you are expected to know is also found in the introductory paragraphs of each Unit.*

  - Note that answers to the tables and questions may not be found in the lab guide, but may be found in the textbook or other resources.

- This is a 3000 level course. As such, you are expected to perform at a high level. This expectation can be summarized in the following explanations and examples:

  - You are asked to name 2 locations where serous membrane can be found. Answering abdominopelvic cavity and peritoneal cavity would NOT be accepted.

  - An almost correct answer isn't correct. Do not expect partial credit if you got part of an answer correct.

  - As a general rule, If the graders are not sure what answer you intended, they will not give you partial credit on the off-chance that what you intended was the correct answer. Put another way – do not expect the benefit of the doubt on grading. For example, if you are asked to identify the femoral artery, and you answer "femoral", we have no way to know whether you thought it was the artery or the vein and you will receive no credit, since for all we know, you may have thought it was the femoral vein. As another example, you are asked to identify the sternothyroid muscle. Your answer reads "sternothyoid". While this answer is only off by 1 letter, it is not clear whether you thought the muscle was the sternothyroid or the sternohyoid. Thus you would receive no credit.

  - Even though a question may not state "be specific", you are expected to provide an answer at the level of detail included in the lab guide. For example, if a synarthrosis is indicated, and you are asked to identify the type of joint and answer "cartilaginous", you will AT MOST receive partial credit.

- Spelling is graded for all answers.
  - Minor spelling errors such as a missing, extra, incorrect, or transposed letters will result in a one-quarter point deduction with a maximum deduction of 8 minor errors, or 2 points out of 80 points possible (2.5% of the exam).
  - One exception to this rule is when a spelling error results in a correct spelling for another anatomical structure. For example, writing ilium (a bone that fuses with the ischium and pubis to form the coxal bone) as "ileum" (a region of the small intestine) would result in no credit for the question.
  - Another exception is outlined above, where a minor spelling answer makes it unclear what you thought the structure was (sternothyoid vs sternothyroid vs sternohyoid)
  - Major spelling errors are answers that are significantly misspelled, but still recognizable as the correct intended anatomical feature. These errors will result in a one-half point deduction with no maximum number of deductions.
  - If an answer is not recognizable as the correct intended anatomical feature, or is unreadable, it will receive no credit. Students have a clipboard and a full minute to fill in each answer; there is no excuse for illegible handwriting.
- If you get marked off for an answer, and can bring in a **CREDIBLE** reference (peer-reviewed or published textbook) that shows your answer is correct, your grade will be adjusted. If there are questions about the resource or how the information is interpreted, the final decision will rest with the lab coordinator or the lecture instructor.
  - This policy reflects the fact that different resources occasionally give different names to the same structure…
- Extra Credit <u>may</u> be offered on the practicals. Students can typically expect **one or two questions worth 1 point** of extra credit per practical. To receive the extra credit, the answer must be **completely** correct with no spelling errors. Extra credit questions that contain multiple parts must include all pertinent information and only correct information. No partial extra credit will be awarded.
- FOR ALL MULTIANSWER QUESTIONS, right and left versions of the same structure will only count as one answer, not two.
  - For example: "Name two bones found in the antebrachial region." Right and left ulna will only count as one of the required bones.
- Be sure to read each question **carefully** and answer <u>only</u> the question being asked.
  - Answers that include more or less information than requested will be evaluated as follows:
    - For answers that provide information beyond what is requested, ½ point will be deducted for each wrong inclusion, *even if the answer includes the appropriate amount of correct information*.
      - For example: a question asks for 2 bones that help form the orbit. An answer of "palatine, frontal, mandible and temporal" would receive no credit. Even though the first two bones fulfill the requirements of the question, the student would lose 1/2 for mandible and 1/2 for the temporal bone because they don't contribute to the orbit.
  - No question will receive less than zero credit.
  - Additional correct description that exceeds what is requested by a question will not affect the awarded credit.

- Questions that require two elements and have only one correct element present will receive half credit. Similarly, if a question asks for 3 elements and only 2 correct answers are given, 2/3rd of a point will be given.
- Abbreviations:
  - The only acceptable abbreviations for practicals are as follows:
    - Left = "l."
    - Right = "r."
    - Artery = "a."
    - Vein = "v."
    - Muscle = "m."
    - Nerve = "n."
    - **Note:** Failure to include right/left or artery/vein, or the correct abbreviation where directed WILL RESULT IN ¼ POINT DEDUCTION, ***unless the omission renders the provided answer incorrect or leaves ambiguity regarding whether or not you knew which structure it was.*** If the omission makes the answer incorrect or ambiguous, the entire point will be deducted.
    - A maximum of 2 points can be deducted for left-right errors. There is no cap on the amount of points that may be deducted for artery-vein-nerve errors.
    - Hormones may be abbreviated with standard accepted abbreviations (ex: FSH, LH, TSH, etc…)
    - Note: though abbreviations such as "MCL" and "ACL" are commonplace, these will NOT be accepted for credit.
- For muscle origins and insertions:
  - To receive full credit, the origin or insertion will need to be identified to the level specified in the lab guide.
    - Identifying the origin or insertion to the level of the correct bone will result in ½ of the possible credit.
    - Another way to think of this is that identifying O/I to the correct bone is worth ½ credit, to the correct feature is worth ½ credit, and where a range is involved, identifying the correct range is worth ½ credit.
    - Regarding identifying correct ranges for O/I: although identifying a portion of the range within the correct range isn't wrong, it also isn't right, so it does not receive credit. For example, if the correct range of origin is T1-T12, and you answer T2-T11, you would lose ½ credit.
- Muscle actions:
  - Typically (though not always!!) questions regarding muscle actions will ask for one of a muscle's actions, not all of its actions.
- Grading examples:
  - "Name vessel A". The station requests that you identify the left gastric artery. You answer "L. gastric". You would lose ¼ point for omitting "artery" or "a" (this answer would not loose full credit as there is no left gastric vein)

- "Name vessel B". The station requests that you identify the superior mesenteric artery. You answer "mesenteric a." and receive no credit because it is unclear whether you understand the difference between the superior and inferior mesenteric arteries. These two arteries supply very different regions of the digestive system, so it is important to name them specifically.

- "Name vessel B". The station requests that you identify the superior mesenteric artery. You answer "superior mesenteric" and receive no credit because it is unclear whether you are able to differentiate between the superior mesenteric artery and the superior mesenteric vein.

- "Name vessel A". The station requests that you identify the left gastric artery. You answer "L. grastic a.". You would lose ¼ point for the spelling error.

- "Name vessel A". The station requests that you identify the left gastric artery. You answer "L grastrin A". You would lose 1/2 for the major spelling error.

- "Name vessel A". The station requests that you identify the left gastric artery. You answer "L grastic A, L gastroepiplic A". You would lose ¾ of a point for the inclusion of one incorrect answer, AND the misspelling.

- "Name vessel A". The station requests that you identify the left gastric artery. You answer "L glastipic A". You would receive no credit since your answer is not recognizable as close to the correct answer.

I, _____ have read and understood the grading policies outlined in this manual.

_____ _____

(signature and date)

V. NOTICE TO STUDENTS WITH LEARNING DISABILITIES

Learning disabled students should identify themselves to the course instructor within the first week of the semester if they have any special disabilities that might influence their performance in the class and if they wish to make special arrangements related to course requirements such as exams.

VI. TAPING LECTURES

Students may tape-record recitation (student right), but first they must sign an agreement that states the fate of such tapes (faculty right), e.g., the tapes may not be duplicated, sold, or distributed in any way and must be destroyed at the end of the semester.

VII. CHEATING

Cheating incidents will be handled through official university channels. **Consistent with the College's Academic Integrity Policy, all violations of this course's academic integrity policy will be reported to the Dean's office. Students who have committed multiple instances of academic dishonesty can be subject to institutional penalties such as probation or suspension, in addition to the penalties for this course. From the Academic *Policies and Regulations* of UCD:**

"In all academic areas it is imperative that work be original, or explicit acknowledgment be given for the use of other persons' ideas or language. Students should consult with instructors to learn specific procedures appropriate for documenting the work of others in each given field. Breaches of academic honesty can result in disciplinary measures ranging from lowering of a grade to permanent compulsory withdrawal from the university."

Please note that "knowingly contributing to another's acts of academic dishonesty" is considered academic dishonesty by the UCD Academic Honor Code. **This means that if you are aware of cheating, and do not report it, you are also guilty of cheating.** All offenses, at the discretion of the instructor, regardless of how minor, may result in a failing grade on that exam and a letter documenting the offense placed in the student's file. Major offenses may result in failure of the class and the pursuit of all applicable university penalties. Please refer to the course syllabus for reiteration and further details on the consequences of academic dishonesty.

VIII. ONE FINAL COMMENT:

The anatomy of the human body is a very complex, yet fascinating, topic. It is not an easy subject to master, but if approached with the proper attitude it can provide you with a lifetime of useful knowledge. Look at the way we are all put together, picture in your mind how each system is working, apply the information to your daily life, and you will find the subject is not as daunting as you once thought.

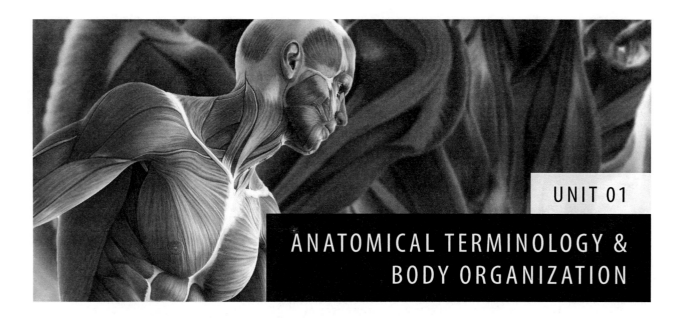

UNIT 01

ANATOMICAL TERMINOLOGY & BODY ORGANIZATION

I. ANATOMICAL TERMS

Just as in any other discipline, anatomy has its own language and terminology. The terminology associated with the study of anatomy is descriptive and precise. This chapter is an important one to master, as you will be using these terms throughout the course.

A. Define the anatomical position.

B. What is the significance of the anatomical position?

C. Directional terms - be sure to realize that all directional terms refer to a body in the anatomical position. Please complete the table below:

Term	Definition	Example
Anterior		
Posterior		
Dorsal		
Ventral		
Medial		
Lateral		
Proximal		
Distal		
Superior		
Inferior		
Cranial (rostral)		

Caudal		
Superficial	located close to or on the body surface	skin is superficial to muscles
Deep	further beneath the body surface than superficial structures	muscles are deep to the skin

D. Planes of section - The body is also studied in different planes that pass through it. A plane is defined as an imaginary flat surface that divides the body. Be able to define and locate the following planes of section on a model or diagram:

Term	Definition
Frontal (coronal)	
Midsagittal (median)	
Parasagittal	
Transverse (horizontal)	Divides the body into superior and inferior sections

II. BODY ORGANIZATION

A. Regional terms – be able to correctly label a diagram using the following terms:

Term	Region	Term	Region
axial	head, neck, and trunk	pollex	
appendicular		umbilical	
orbital		abdominal	
buccal		inguinal	
oral		pubic	
cervical		femoral	
acromial		popliteal	
thoracic		patellar	
axillary		peroneal (fibular)	lateral side of leg

brachial		calcaneal	
antecubital		plantar	
antebrachial		hallux	
sural		crural	

B. Be able to locate the following body cavities on a model, the skeleton, or a diagram. You must also be able to name the contents of these body cavities:

1. dorsal body cavity
   a. cranial cavity
      contents=

   b. spinal cavity
      contents=

2. ventral body cavity
   a. thoracic cavity

      i. pleural cavities (2)
      ii. mediastinum
         1. pericardial cavity (contains heart)
         2. thymus, trachea, esophagus, and aorta are also contained within the mediastinum
   b. abdominopelvic cavity
      i. abdominal cavity
         contents=

      ii. pelvic cavity
         contents=

C. Know these serous membranes associated with the ventral body cavity and the structures/areas they cover.
   a. pericardium
   b. pleurae
   c. peritoneum

Each type of serous membrane has a **visceral layer which lies on the organ, and a **parietal** layer which lines the body cavity.

TERMINOLOGY STUDY QUESTIONS

1. Complete the sentences below with the appropriate directional term(s).

    A. The esophagus is _____ to the trachea.

    B. In correct anatomical position, the thumb is _____ to all the fingers of the hand

    C. The diaphragm is _____ to the heart

    D. The head is _____ to the neck

    E. In relation to the shoulder, the elbow is more _____ than the hand.

    F. The skin of the thigh is _____ to the femur.

    G. The pleural cavity is _____ to the ribs and sternum

2. Complete the sentences below with the appropriate plane of section.

    A. The _____ plane separates the body into superior and inferior portions.

    B. The _____ plane separates the body into equal left and right halves.

    C. The _____ plane separates the body into anterior and posterior portions.

    D. The _____ plane separates the body into right and left portions.

3. Match the correct regional term for the each area listed below.

    A. eye   **i.** axillary

    B. arm pit   **ii.** antebrachial

    C. forearm   **iii.** hallux

    D. navel   **iv.** peroneal

    E. lateral side of the leg   **v.** umbilical

    F. big toe   **vi.** orbital

4. List the cavities located within the abdominopelvic cavity and the contents of each:

    A. _____

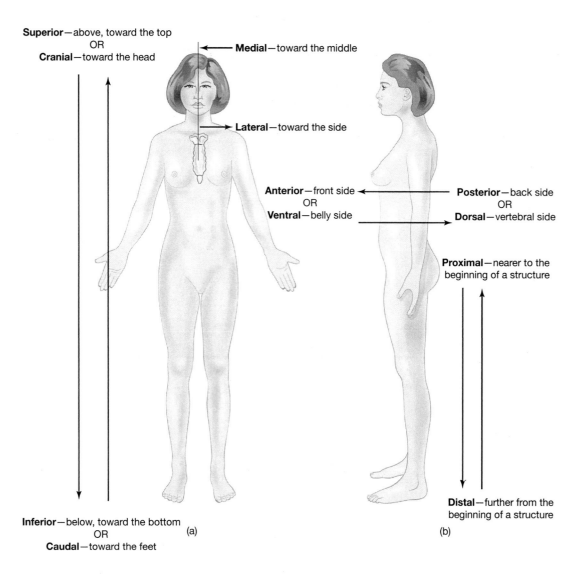

Superior—above, toward the top
OR
Cranial—toward the head

Medial—toward the middle

Lateral—toward the side

Anterior—front side
OR
Ventral—belly side

Posterior—back side
OR
Dorsal—vertebral side

Proximal—nearer to the beginning of a structure

Distal—further from the beginning of a structure

Inferior—below, toward the bottom
OR
Caudal—toward the feet

(a)

(b)

Figure 1-1. Directional terms

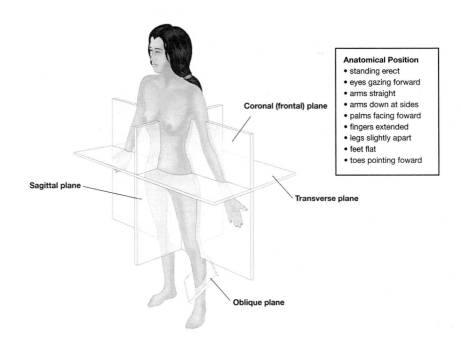

Anatomical Position
- standing erect
- eyes gazing forward
- arms straight
- arms down at sides
- palms facing foward
- fingers extended
- legs slightly apart
- feet flat
- toes pointing foward

Coronal (frontal) plane

Sagittal plane

Transverse plane

Oblique plane

Figure 1-2. Planes of human body in anatomical position

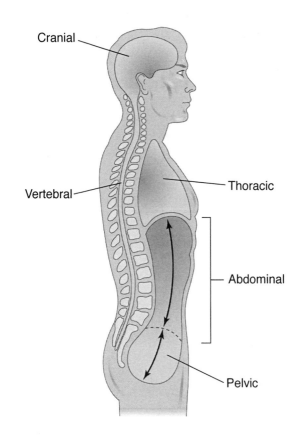

Cranial

Vertebral

Thoracic

Abdominal

Pelvic

Figure 1-3. Body cavities

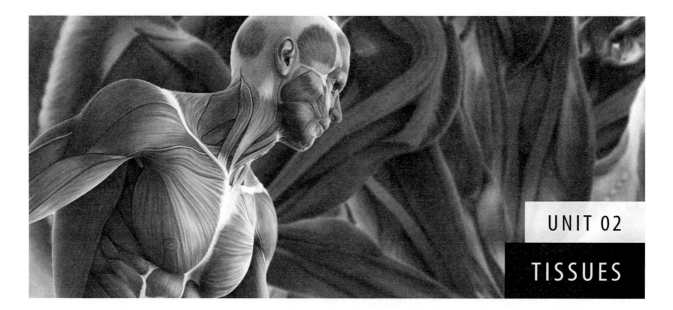

UNIT 02

TISSUES

I. Cells are independent, LIVE entities that, working together, make the entire human body. However, the body is NOT simply an accumulation of hundreds of different cell types, all jumbled together, each working independently. Within the body, specific, separate types of cells which are often similar in structure, and almost always similar in function, group together to form tissues. Tissues are collections of similar cells, all cooperating to perform a specific function. Within a given organ, different types of tissues will be grouped together, so that all of the cells of the different tissues can together perform the function of the organ.

You are responsible for 1) knowing the four primary tissue types, 2) being able to differentiate them based on their characteristics, 3) knowing the sub-types within each classification, 4) knowing the basic function of each tissue, 5) being able to give one or two examples of where each tissue is found in the human body, and 6) being able to identify a given tissue by looking at a picture or a slide of it. **Please note: you will use the images from the textbook, atlas, and slides for identifying what individual tissues look like. These are the images that will be used to test your understanding during the lab practical.**

A. Epithelia

• What are characteristics of epithelia, in general??

• What are its primary functions?

1. Simple squamous epithelium

• Characteristics =

• Location =

• Function =

2. Simple cuboidal epithelium

   • Characteristics =

   • Location =

   • Function =

3. Simple columnar epithelium

   • Characteristics =

   • Location =

   • Function =

4. Pseudostratified columnar epithelium

   • Characteristics =

   • Location =

   • Function =

5. Stratified squamous epithelium

   • Characteristics =

   • Location =

   • Function =

6. Stratified cuboidal epithelium

   • Characteristics =

   • Location =

   • Function =

7. Stratified columnar epithelium

- Characteristics =

- Location =

- Function =

8. Transitional epithelium

- Characteristics =

- Location =

- Function =

B. Connective tissue
- What are the characteristics of CT in general?

- What are its primary functions?

- List the names of some of the CT cells…

- What is extracellular matrix, what is it made of , and what does it do?

1. CT Proper
   a. Loose CT
      i. Areolar
         - Characteristics =

         - Location =

         - Function =

    ii.   Adipose

- Characteristics =

- Location =

- Function =

    iii. Reticular

- Characteristics =

- Location =

- Function =

b.   Dense CT (also called fibrous CT)

    i.   Dense regular

- Characteristics =

- Location =

- Function =

    ii.   Dense irregular

- Characteristics =

- Location =

- Function =

    iii. Elastic

- Characteristics =

- Location =

- Function =

2. Cartilage

    a. Hyaline

        • Characteristics =

        • Location =

        • Function =

    b. Elastic

        • Characteristics =

        • Location =

        • Function =

    c. Fibrocartilage

        • Characteristics =

        • Location =

        • Function =

3. Bone

    • Characteristics =

    • Function =

4. Blood

    • Characteristics =

    • Function =

C. Nervous tissue

- What types of cells make up nervous tissue?

- What is the function of nervous tissue?

- Where is it located?

D. Muscle

- What does it do?

1. Skeletal muscle

   - Characteristics =

   - Location =

   - Function =

2. Cardiac muscle

   - Characteristics =

   - Location =

   - Function =

3. Smooth muscle

   - Characteristics =

   - Location =

   - Function =

II. Epithelial membranes cover surfaces of the body and line body cavities. They are always composed of an epithelium overlying connective tissue, with a basement membrane sandwiched between. You are responsible for knowing 1) the three types of epithelial membranes, 2) where each membrane is found, and 3) in general, what tissues compose them.

A. Basement membrane – lies between the epithelium and the connective tissue of an epithelial membrane. It has two layers:

1. basal lamina

2. reticular lamina

Draw an epithelial membrane including the layers of the basement membrane:

B. 3 epithelial membranes:

1. cutaneous membrane

   • where is it found?

   • what tissues (be specific) compose it?

2. serous membrane (also called serosae)

   • where is it found?

   • what tissues (be specific) compose it?

3. mucous membrane (also called mucosa)

   • where is it found?

   • what tissues (be specific) compose it?

TISSUE STUDY QUESTIONS

1. What characteristics of epithelium make it suited to transport?

2. What is extracellular matrix? What tissue produces it? What is it made of?

3. Why is blood a connective tissue?

4. What are some characteristics of nervous tissue that are unique?

5. Differentiate between smooth, skeletal, and cardiac muscle on the basis of characteristics and function.

6. What is the basement membrane, where is it, and what does it do?

7. Glands, both exo- and endocrine, are formed from epithelia. Why does this make sense?

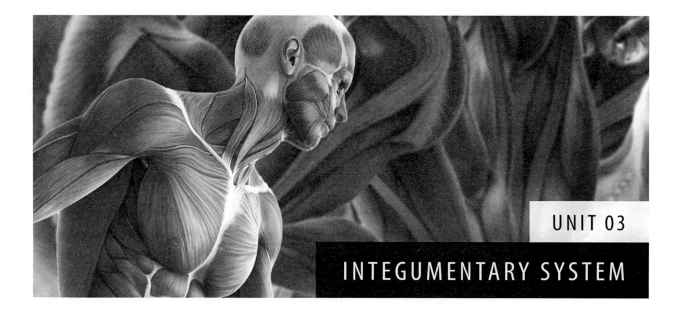

UNIT 03

INTEGUMENTARY SYSTEM

I.   The skin is composed of two different layers, the superficial **epidermis** and deeper **dermis**. Underlying the skin is the **hypodermis**, which is also referred to as superficial fascia, or subcutaneous layer. Be able to identify the following structures of the skin on models, histological slides, and diagrams:

   A. Epidermis - the epidermis is layered; thin skin possesses four layers, while thick skin has five.

   What type of epithelium is the epidermis?_____

   1. stratum germinativum (basale)

      a.   Name two cell types found in this layer

   2. stratum spinosum
      a.   Name one cell type found in this layer

      b.   What feature of this layer gives it its name?

   3. stratum granulosum
      a.   What characteristic of these cells gives this layer its name?

   4. stratum lucidum
      a.   Which type of skin lacks this layer?

   5. stratum corneum

B. Dermis - like the epidermis the dermis is layered, but has only two layers.
   1. papillary layer (areolar connective tissue)
      a. dermal papillae

   2. reticular layer (dense irregular connective tissue)

C. Hypodermis - unlike the two layers of the skin, the deeper hypodermis is not layered. It consists mostly of areolar and adipose tissue, blood vessels, and some sensory receptors. The hypodermis may also contain Pacinian corpuscles.

D. Glands - you will need to be familiar with the distribution of each type and generally what they secrete.
   1. sebaceous
   2. sudoriferous
      a. apocrine
      b. eccrine

E. Sense receptors - for each, you should know their location and general function.
   1. Meissner's corpuscles
   2. Pacinian corpuscles
   3. Ruffini endings (bulbous corpuscles)
   4. free nerve endings
   5. root hair plexus

F. Hair
   1. root
   2. bulb
   3. shaft
   4. arrector pili muscle

Use the space below to draw and label a section of skin:

INTEGUMENTARY STUDY QUESTIONS

1. In which layer of skin are Meissner's corpuscles found? _____

2. Name the 5 layers of the epidermis found in thick skin in order from most superficial to deepest.

    A. _____

    B. _____

    C. _____

    D. _____

    E. _____

3. Name the 3 primary structures that constitute a hair follicle.

    A. _____

    B. _____

    C. _____

4. Name the 2 glands found in the reticular layer of the skin.

    A. _____

    B. _____

UNIT 04

SKELETAL SYSTEM

I. GENERAL CHARACTERISTICS

A. Classification – bones are classified regionally as part of the axial skeleton or the appendicular skeleton, or according to their shape. Given any bone you must be able to classify it according to its shape. Fill in the table below using your text:

Shape of Bone	Definition	Examples
Long		
Short		
Sesamoid (type of short bone)		
Flat	thin, flattened and somewhat curved	sternum, scapula, ribs, most cranial bones
Irregular		
Sutural (type of irregular bone)		

B. Gross anatomy of a long bone - be able to identify the following structures of a long bone on a diagram or specimen (cow bone):
   diaphysis
   epiphyseal line (adult)
   epiphyseal cartilage (juvenile)
   epiphysis (proximal or distal)
   articular cartilage
   periosteum

spongy bone
compact bone
medullary cavity (marrow cavity)
red marrow
yellow marrow

Draw a x-section of a long bone to the right and label all the parts:

C. Bone markings - the surfaces of bones show various bumps, irregularities, holes, and grooves. Be able to define the terms in the following table that apply to bone anatomy. Most of these surface markings can be classified into one of the following three categories:
   1) sites for muscle, ligament or tendon attachment
   2) grooves and holes which allow for passage of blood vessels or nerves
   3) areas that participate in articulations (joints).

As you study specific bones of the human skeleton you will identify examples of each marking. As you start identifying specific bone markings, try to visualize how that structure is used and place it into one of the above functional categories. Use your text to help fill in the table below.

	Marking	Definition	Example
Muscle & Ligament Attachment	Tuberosity		
	Crest		
	Trochanter		
	Tubercle		
	Epicondyle	raised area on or above condyle	lateral epicondyle of humerus
	Line		
	Process		
	Spine		

Parts of Joints	Head		
	Facet		
	Condyle	rounded projection at the end of a bone	medial condyle of femur
	Ramus		
	Fossa		
Path for Vessel or Nerve	Foramen		
	Meatus (= canal)		
	Fissure		
	Groove		
Open Spaces	Sinus	air-filled cavity within a bone	maxillary sinus
	Air cells		

D. Microscopic anatomy of compact bone - The basic structural and functional unit of compact bone is the **osteon** or **Haversian system**. Bone is continually remodeled throughout life, going through a process of bone breakdown (reabsorption) and deposition. The basic functional unit of this process is the osteon. Be able to identify the following features of compact bone on models and figures:

1. central (Haversian) canal
2. concentric lamella(*e*)
3. lacuna(*e*)
4. osteocyte
5. canaliculus (*canaliculi*)
6. perforating (Volkmann's) canal
7. circumferential lamella(e)
8. interstitial lamella(e)

Draw an osteon below and label all the parts:

E. Bone membranes - Connective tissues membranes surround and support bone. Be able to identify:

1. periosteum
2. endosteum
3. Sharpey's fibers (perforating fibers)

F. Bone cells - Throught life, bone cells generate, maintain, and remodel bone. Be able to differentiate the following bone cells based on their function and location.

1. osteocyte
2. osteoblast
3. osteoclast

II. AXIAL SKELETON

The axial skeleton is the skeleton of the head and trunk. It consists of the bones of the skull, thorax, and vertebral column.

   A. Skull - composed of the cranium and facial bones. It is important to recognize that some of the bones of the skull are paired and some are not.

   1. cranium - formed by eight flat bones that articulate at sutures. Identify the following bones, their markings and features:

   a. frontal (1) -
   supraorbital margin (ridge)
   supraorbital foramen
   glabella
   frontal sinuses
   zygomatic process
   nasal process
   maxillary process

   b. parietal (2)

   c. temporal (2) - the temporal bone has four major named regions. Identify these four regions and their associated markings:
   squamous region -
   zygomatic process
   mandibular fossa
   petrous region -
   internal acoustic (auditory) meatus (canal)
   jugular foramen
   foramen lacerum
   carotid canal
   mastoid region -
   mastoid process
   mastoid air cells
   stylomastoid foramen
   tympanic region -
   external acoustic (auditory) meatus (canal)
   styloid process

   d. occipital (1) -
   foramen magnum
   occipital condyles
   hypoglossal canal
   external occipital protuberance

   e. sphenoid (1) -
   body
   lesser wings
   greater wings
   pterygoid processes
   sella turcica
   sphenoid sinuses
   optic foramen
   superior orbital fissure

foramen rotundum

foramen ovale

foramen spinosum

 f. ethmoid (1) -

  cribriform plate

  crista galli

  perpendicular plate - along with the vomer and hyaline
   cartilage forms the nasal septum

  ethmoid sinuses

  superior nasal concha(*e*)

  middle nasal concha(*e*)

  olfactory foramina

2. facial bones

 a. maxilla(*e*) (2) -

  alveolar margin

  alveolar process

  frontal process

  zygomatic process

  palatine process

  infraorbital foramen

  inferior orbital fissure

  maxillary sinus

 b. mandible (1) -

  body

  ramus (*rami*)

  mandibular angle

  mandibular condyle

  coronoid process

  mandibular notch

  mental foramen

  mandibular foramen

  alveolar margin

  alveolar process

 c. zygomatic (2) -

  temporal process - along with the zygomatic process of the temporal bone
  forms the **zygomatic arch**

   frontal process

   maxillary process

 d. palatine (2) -

  horizontal plate - along with the palatine process of the maxillary bone forms
  the **hard palate**

   perpendicular plate

   orbital process

 e. lacrimal (2)

 f. nasal (2)

 g. vomer (1)

 h. inferior nasal concha(*e*) (2)

i. hyoid -
   lesser horn (cornu)
   greater horn (cornu)

3. skull characteristics and features -
   a. paranasal sinuses **-** be able to locate and identify the following paranasal sinuses:
      frontal
      ethmoid
      maxillary
      sphenoid

   b. sutures - be able to identify the following sutures and which bones articulate at a given suture:
      sagittal -

      coronal -

      squamous -

      lambdoid -

      occipitomastoid -

   c. cranial fossae - be able to identify and name the bones that form the three cranial fossae. You must also be able to state which major brain structures are located in each cranial fossa.

Fossa	Formed by	Contains
Anterior		
Middle		
Posterior	occipital bone	cerebellum

   d. orbits - the bony cavities that house the eyes and associated muscles, blood vessels, and nerves. You must know which bones form the wall of the orbits.

Orbit wall	Bones forming orbit wall
Roof	
Medial wall	sphenoid, ethmoid, maxilla, lacrimal
Lateral wall	
Floor	

B. Vertebral column
1. general characteristics
    a. consists of 26 bones separated into five major divisions:
        1. cervical
        2. thoracic
        3. lumbar
        4. sacral
        5. coccygeal
    b. Vertebrae are separated from one another by an **intervertebral disc**, which consists of an outer layer of fibrocartilage called **annulus fibrosis**, and an inner gelatinous core called **nucleus pulposus.**
    c. The adult vertebral column exhibits four main curvatures:
       Primary curvature:
        1. thoracic vertebrae
        2. sacral vertebrae
       Secondary curvature:
        3. cervical vertebrae
        4. lumbar vertebrae

Define the difference between a primary and secondary curvature:

Why (and when) does a cervical curvature develop?

Why (and when) does a lumbar curvature develop?

    d. be able to identify the following features common to all vertebrae:
       body (centrum)
       vertebral arch
           pedicle
           lamina(e)
       vertebral foramen (contains the spinal cord)
       intervertebral foramen (transmits spinal nerves)
       spinous process
       transverse process
       inferior articular process
       superior articular process

2. cervical vertebrae (C_1-C_7) - be able to identify the features specific to the cervical
    vertebrae:
    > atlas - the first cervical vertebra
    >> unique characteristics:
    >> *has no body
    >> *has anterior and posterior arches
    > axis - the second cervical vertebra
    >> unique characteristic:
    >> *has an **odontoid process** (dens)
    > features unique to vertebrae C1-C7 -
    >> transverse foramina (transmits the vertebral arteries)
    >> bifid spinous process
    > vertebra prominens - vertebra C_7, you can palpate this on yourself

3. thoracic vertebrae (T_1-T_{12}) -
    > superior and inferior demifacets
    >> function: to articulate with the head of a rib; "demi" refers to the fact that
    >> the head of the rib articulates with two vertebrae, leaving half a facet on each
    >> one
    >> *present on T_1-T_9
    > full facet
    >> function: also for head of rib articulation; these are whole facets since the
    >> head of the rib articulates with the body of only one vertebra
    >> *present on T_1, T_{10}, T_{11}, T_{12}
    > transverse costal facet for <u>tubercle</u> of a rib
    >> function: articulation site for tubercle of a rib
    >> *present on T_1 - T_{10}

4. lumbar vertebrae (L_1- L_5) - know how many there are and where they are located. Be able
    to distinguish from a thoracic vertebra.
    > *lacks demifacets for rib articulation

5. sacrum (S_1 - S_5) - formed by the fusion of five sacral vertebrae. Be able to identify the
    following features of the sacrum:
    >> superior articular process
    >> sacral canal
    >> sacral promontory
    >> ala
    >> transverse lines (also called transverse ridges)
    >> sacral foramina
    >> median sacral crest
    >> sacral hiatus
    >> auricular surface of sacrum

6. coccyx – usually 4 fused vertebrae (can range from 3-5)

C. Thorax - the bony thorax consists of the sternum (breastbone), ribs and their associated costal cartilages, and the thoracic vertebrae.

Which body cavity does the thorax house?

1. sternum - the sternum consists of three sections, the manubrium, body, and xiphoid process. Be able to identify the following:

manubrium -
jugular notch (suprasternal notch)
body -
sternal angle (the angle made between the manubrium and body of the sternum)

Try to find your own sternal angle. Look at an articulated skeleton. Can you guess the clinical usefulness of the angle?

xiphoid process

2. ribs - there are twelve **pairs** of ribs, the first seven are true ribs, the inferior five are false ribs. The most inferior 2 pairs of ribs are also called floating ribs.

What are the differences between true, false, and floating ribs?

Be able to identify the following features common to all ribs:
head
neck
articular tubercle (tuberculum)/costal tubercle/tubercle of rib
costal angle
costal groove
shaft

III. APPENDICULAR SKELETON

The appendicular skeleton consists of the bones of the limbs and their attachments to the axial skeleton. The upper limbs are attached to the axial skeleton by the pectoral girdle, while the lower limbs are secured to the axial skeleton by the pelvic girdle.

A. Pectoral Girdle
1. clavicle -
sternal end
acromial end
2. scapula(*e*) -
borders -
superior
medial (vertebral)
lateral (axillary)

angles -
    superior
    inferior
features -
    acromion process
    coracoid process
    suprascapular notch
    glenoid fossa (cavity)
    infraglenoid tubercle
    supraglenoid tubercle
    spine
    supraspinous fossa
    infraspinous fossa
    subscapular fossa

B. Upper limb
  1. humerus -
    proximal end (articulates with the glenoid fossa of the scapula) -
      head
      greater tubercle
      lesser tubercle
      intertubercular groove (sulcus)
      anatomical neck
      surgical neck
    shaft -
      deltoid tuberosity
      radial groove
    distal end (articulates with ulna and radius of the forearm) -
      trochlea
      capitulum
      medial epicondyle
      lateral epicondyle
      coronoid fossa
      olecranon fossa
      radial fossa
      lateral supracondylar ridge
      medial supracondylar ridge

  2. radius-
    proximal end (articulates with the humerus and ulna) -
      head
      neck
      radial tuberosity
    shaft -
      interosseous border
    distal end (articulates with ulna, scaphoid, and lunate) -
      ulnar notch
      styloid process

3. ulna-
>proximal end (articulates with humerus and radius) -
>>olecranon process
>>coronoid process
>>trochlear notch
>>radial notch
>shaft -
>>interosseous border
>distal end (articulates with radius) -
>>head
>>styloid process

C. Hand
>1. carpals (wrist) - consists of eight short bones
>>proximal row (from lateral to medial) -
>>>scaphoid
>>>lunate
>>>triquetral (triangular)
>>>pisiform
>>distal row -
>>>trapezium
>>>trapezoid
>>>capitate
>>>hamate

There are many useful mnemonics that can be used to help you remember the carpal bones. Use the "clean" version below (or one of the more colorful version!):

Sally   - scaphoid
Left   - lunate
The   - triangular
Party   - pisiform
To   - trapezium
Take   - trapezoid
Connie - capitate
Home   - hamate

>2. metacarpals -
>>five per hand (numbered 1st-5th beginning on lateral side of hand)
>>>base
>>>head

>3. phalanges -
>>three per digit
>>>proximal
>>>middle [no middle phalanx of the pollex(thumb)]
>>>distal

Which of the carpal bones articulates with the radius?

D. Pelvic girdle - the pelvic girdle is formed by two coxal bones. Each coxal bone is composed of three separate bones that fuse during childhood: the **ilium, ischium** and **pubis**. In adults, the boundaries of these bones are indistinguishable; however, the original bone names remain as corresponding regions of the coxal bone.

    1. coxal bone -

        a. ilium (superior flared portion of the coxal bone) -

            ala
            iliac crest
            anterior superior iliac spine
            posterior superior iliac spine
            anterior inferior iliac spine
            posterior inferior iliac spine
            greater sciatic notch
            iliac fossa
            arcuate line
            acetabulum (all three regions of the coxal bone contribute to the acetabulum)
            auricular surface of ilium

        b. ischium (inferior and posterior part of the coxal bone) -

        body
        ischial ramus
        ischial spine
        ischial tuberosity (when you sit you are sitting on your ischial tuberosities)
        lesser sciatic notch

        c. pubis (anterior portion of the coxal bone) -

        superior ramus of pubis
        inferior ramus of pubis
        body
        pubic crest
        pubic tubercle
        obturator foramen
        pubic symphysis
        pectineal line

2. pelvic cavity - the bony pelvis is divided into two parts by a rim-like structure called the **pelvic brim** which is a continous oval ridge that runs from the pubic crest through the pectineal line of the pubis, arcuate line of the ilium, the rounded inferior edge of the sacral ala, and the sacral promontory. The false pelvis lies above the brim and is part of the abdominal cavity. The true pelvis lies below the brim and <u>is</u> the pelvic cavity.

   a. true pelvis - bowl-shaped structure which houses the lower portions of the gastrointestinal and urinary tracts, and the internal organs of reproduction.
   b. pelvic inlet - opening that has the pelvic brim as the boundaries
   c. pelvic outlet - the inferior boundary of the true pelvis, formed by coccyx posteriorly, ischial tuberosities laterally, pubic arch anteriorly.
   d. female pelvis vs. male pelvis - you should be able to distinguish between a female and male pelvis, paying particular attention to the differences in the pelvic inlets and outlets. Using information found in your textbook fill in the following table:

Characteristics of the Male and Female Pelvis

Characteristic	Female	Male
Structural and functional differences	tilted _____ cavity _____ _____ adapted for _____	tilted _____ cavity _____ _____ adapted for _____
Bone thickness		
Acetabulum	relative size _____ distance between _____	relative size _____ distance between _____
Pubic angle/ arch		
Pelvic inlet	shape _____	shape _____
Pelvic outlet	shape _____	shape _____

E. Lower limb
1. femur-
    proximal end (articulates with the acetabulum) -
        head
        fovea capitis
        neck
        greater trochanter
        lesser trochanter
        intertrochanteric line
        intertrochanteric crest
    shaft -
        gluteal tuberosity
        linea aspera
    distal end (articulates with the tibia) -
        lateral condyle
        medial condyle
        intercondylar notch (fossa)
        lateral epicondyle
        medial epicondyle
        patellar surface
        adductor tubercle

2. patella -
    apex
    base
    articular surface

3. tibia-
    proximal end (articulates with the femur and fibula) -
        medial condyle
        lateral condyle
        intercondylar eminence
        tibial tuberosity
    shaft -
        anterior crest
    distal end (articulates with the talus and fibula) -
        medial malleolus
        fibular notch

4. fibula-
    proximal end (articulates with the tibia) -
        head
    distal end (articulates with the talus and tibia) -
        lateral malleolus

F. Foot
1. tarsus (ankle) -
    talus
    calcaneus
    navicular

medial cuneiform
intermediate cuneiform
lateral cuneiform
cuboid

There are many useful mnemonics that can be used to help you remember the tarsal bones. Use the one below, or come up with one of your own:

Tiger   - talus
Cubs   - calcaneus
Need   - navicular
M   - medial cuneiform
I   - intermediate cuneiform
L   - lateral cuneiform
C   - cuboid

2. metatarsals - five per foot
    base
    head

3. phalanges - three per toe
    proximal
    middle [no middle phalanx of the hallux (big toe)]
    distal

SKELETAL SYSTEM STUDY QUESTIONS

1. How many total true ribs are there? _____ False ribs? _____ Floating ribs? _____

2. TRUE or FALSE: The medullary cavity of a long bone is found in the diaphysis.

3. The basic structural and functional unit of compact bone is the _____.

4. Name the 2 bones that comprise the hard palate.

   A. _____

   B. _____

5. Name 2 structures found in the squamous region of the temporal bone.

   A. _____

   B. _____

6. Name the bone(s) that form the medial wall of the orbit.

7. The outer layer of an intervertebral disc comprised of fibrocartilage is called the _____ _____.

8. TRUE or FALSE: Transverse costal facets are found on vertebrae T1 – T12.

9. Name the 3 bones that comprise the coxal bone.

   A. _____

   B. _____

   C. _____

10. The proximal end of the tibia articulates with which 2 bones?

   A. _____

   B. _____

11. Name the 2 bones that form the zygomatic arch.

     A. _____

     B. _____

12. What bone(s) articulate(s) with the head of the radius?

13. The gluteal tuberosity is found on which bone?

14. Fill in the missing names:

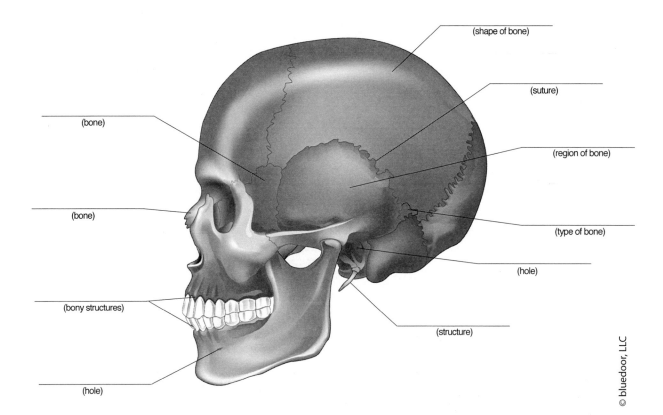

(shape of bone)

(suture)

(bone)

(region of bone)

(bone)

(type of bone)

(hole)

(bony structures)

(structure)

(hole)

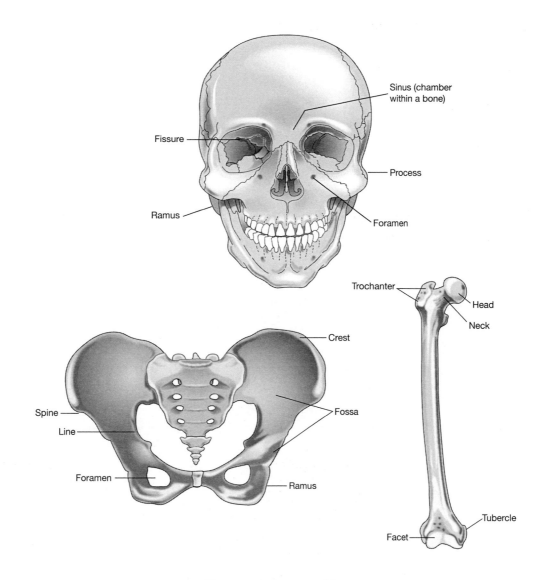

Figure 4-1. Bone markings

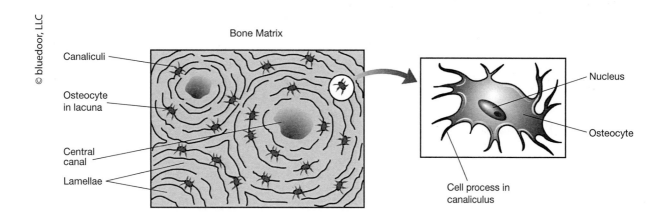

Figure 4-2. Compact bone and the osteon

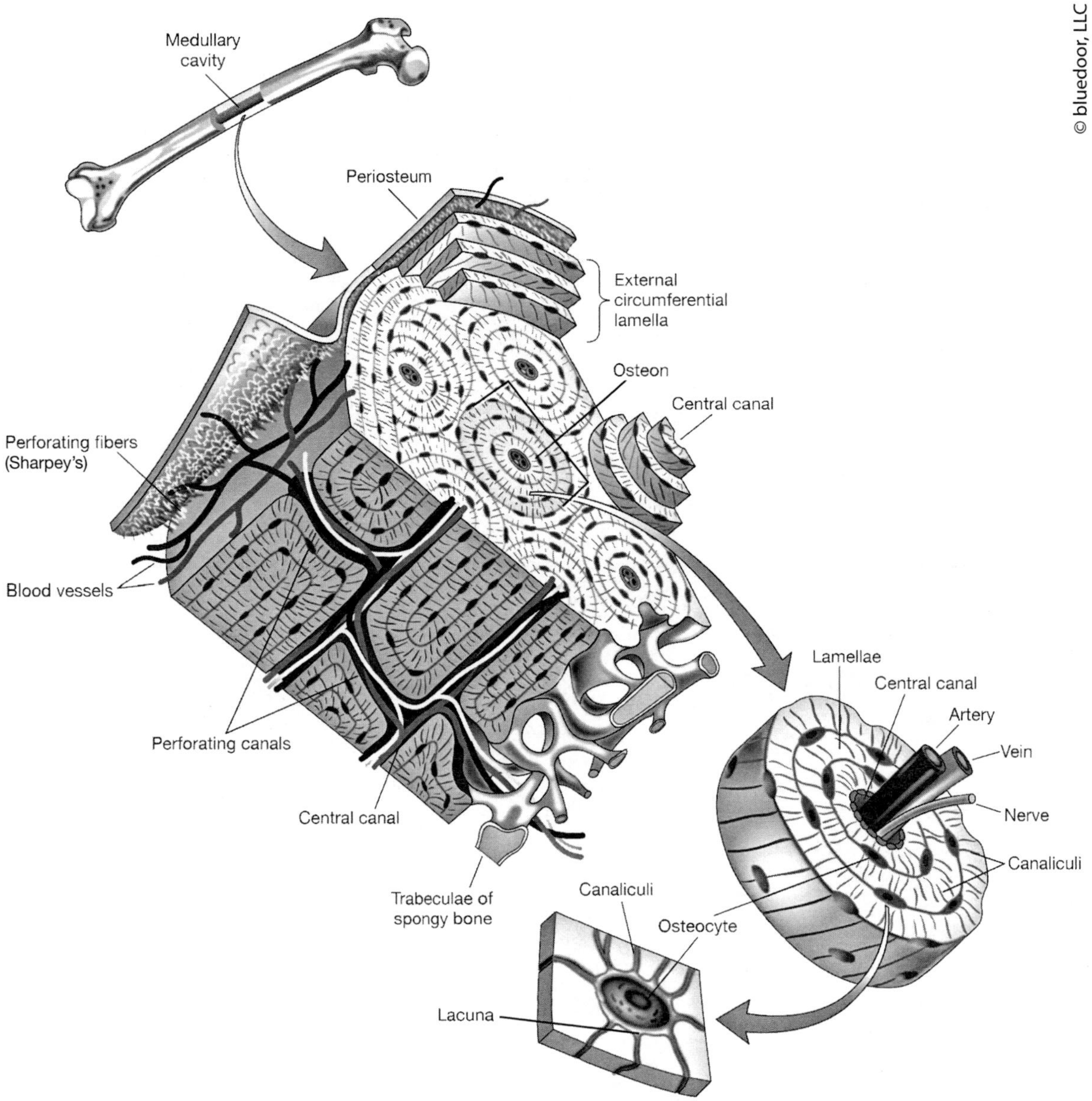

Figure 4-3. Compact bone tissue

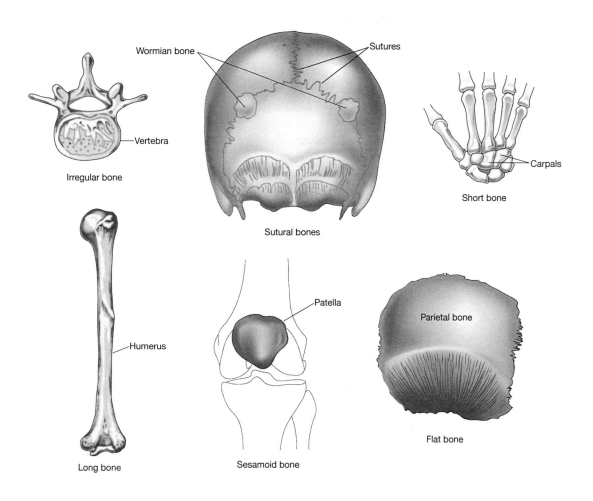

Figure 4-4. Bone shapes

Long Bone, Longitudinal

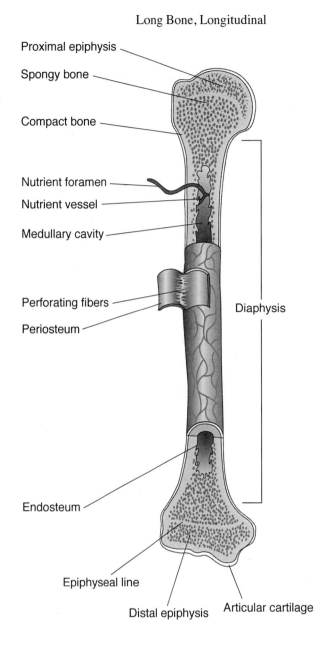

Proximal epiphysis

Spongy bone

Compact bone

Nutrient foramen

Nutrient vessel

Medullary cavity

Perforating fibers

Periosteum

Diaphysis

Endosteum

Epiphyseal line

Distal epiphysis

Articular cartilage

Figure 4-5. Gross anatomy of a long bone

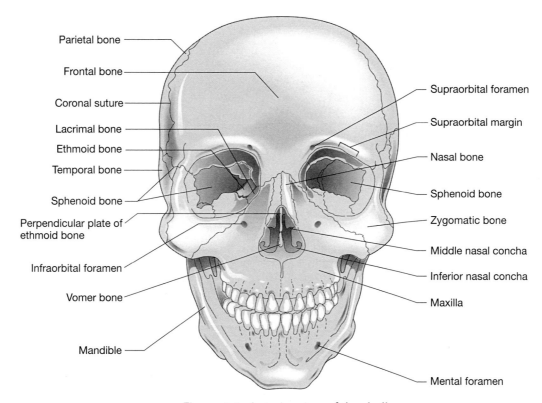

Parietal bone

Frontal bone

Coronal suture

Lacrimal bone

Ethmoid bone

Temporal bone

Sphenoid bone

Perpendicular plate of
ethmoid bone

Infraorbital foramen

Vomer bone

Mandible

Supraorbital foramen

Supraorbital margin

Nasal bone

Sphenoid bone

Zygomatic bone

Middle nasal concha

Inferior nasal concha

Maxilla

Mental foramen

Figure 4-6. Anterior view of the skull

Skull, Lateral View

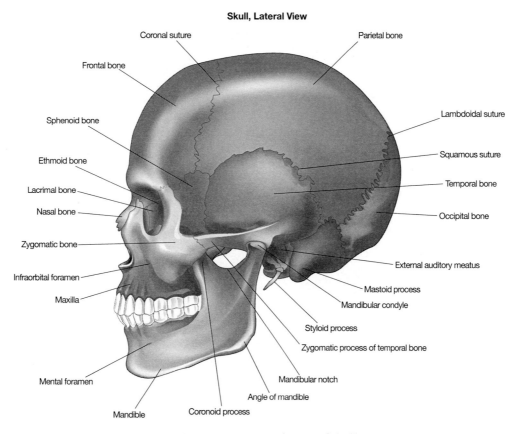

Coronal suture

Frontal bone

Sphenoid bone

Ethmoid bone

Lacrimal bone

Nasal bone

Zygomatic bone

Infraorbital foramen

Maxilla

Mental foramen

Mandible

Coronoid process

Angle of mandible

Mandibular notch

Coronoid process

Zygomatic process of temporal bone

Styloid process

Mandibular condyle

Mastoid process

External auditory meatus

Occipital bone

Temporal bone

Squamous suture

Lambdoidal suture

Parietal bone

Figure 4-7. Lateral view of skull

Skull, Midsagittal View

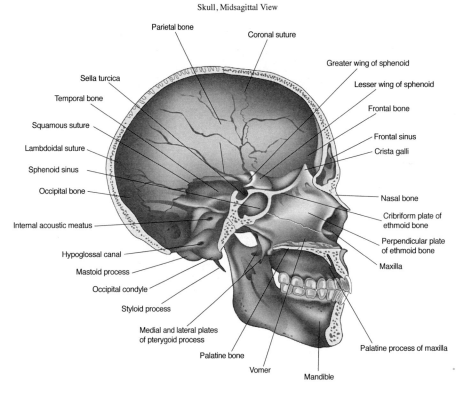

Parietal bone

Coronal suture

Sella turcica

Temporal bone

Squamous suture

Lambdoidal suture

Sphenoid sinus

Occipital bone

Internal acoustic meatus

Hypoglossal canal

Mastoid process

Occipital condyle

Styloid process

Medial and lateral plates
of pterygoid process

Palatine bone

Vomer

Mandible

Greater wing of sphenoid

Lesser wing of sphenoid

Frontal bone

Frontal sinus

Crista galli

Nasal bone

Cribriform plate of
ethmoid bone

Perpendicular plate
of ethmoid bone

Maxilla

Palatine process of maxilla

Figure 4-8. Midsagittal view of skull

Floor of Cranial Cavity

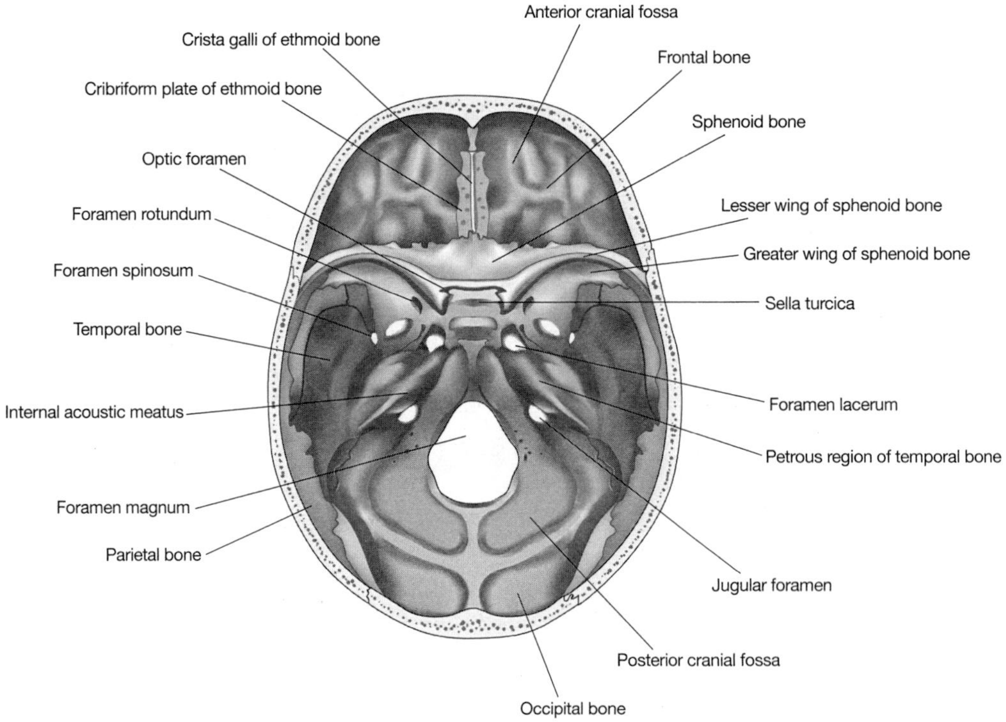

Crista galli of ethmoid bone

Cribriform plate of ethmoid bone

Optic foramen

Foramen rotundum

Foramen spinosum

Temporal bone

Internal acoustic meatus

Foramen magnum

Parietal bone

Anterior cranial fossa

Frontal bone

Sphenoid bone

Lesser wing of sphenoid bone

Greater wing of sphenoid bone

Sella turcica

Foramen lacerum

Petrous region of temporal bone

Jugular foramen

Posterior cranial fossa

Occipital bone

Figure 4-9. Superior view of cranium

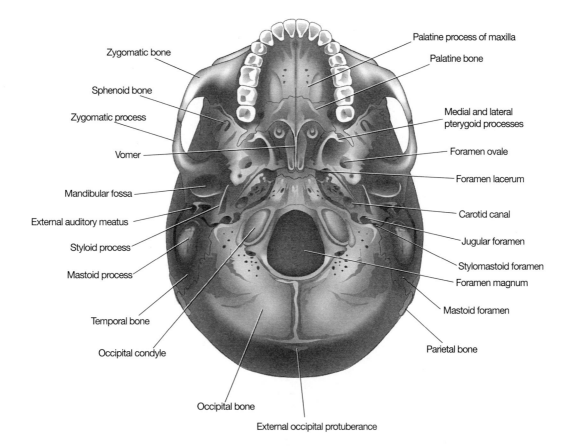

Zygomatic bone

Sphenoid bone

Zygomatic process

Vomer

Mandibular fossa

External auditory meatus

Styloid process

Mastoid process

Temporal bone

Occipital condyle

Palatine process of maxilla

Palatine bone

Medial and lateral pterygoid processes

Foramen ovale

Foramen lacerum

Carotid canal

Jugular foramen

Stylomastoid foramen

Foramen magnum

Mastoid foramen

Parietal bone

Occipital bone

External occipital protuberance

Figure 4-10. Inferior view of skull

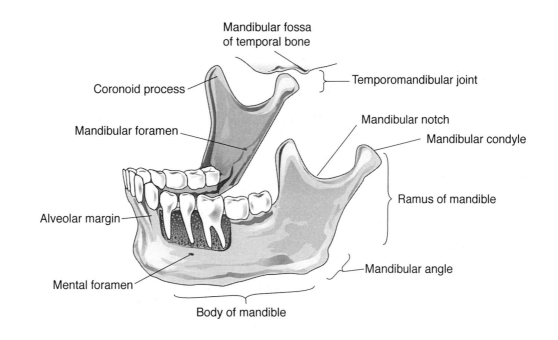

Mandibular fossa of temporal bone

Coronoid process

Mandibular foramen

Alveolar margin

Mental foramen

Temporomandibular joint

Mandibular notch

Mandibular condyle

Ramus of mandible

Mandibular angle

Body of mandible

Figure 4-11. The mandible

Adult Vertebral Column

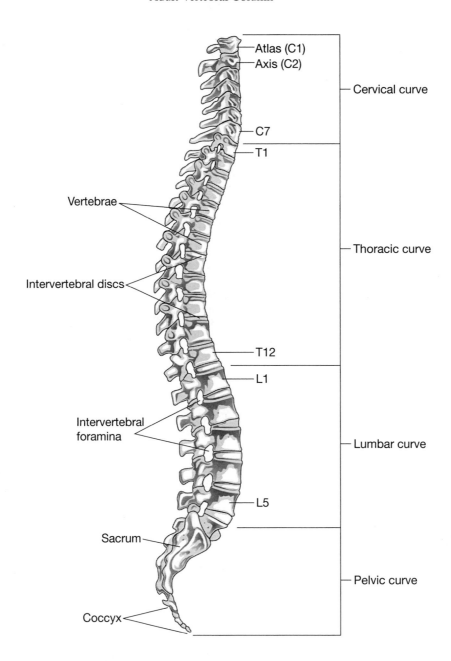

- Atlas (C1)
- Axis (C2)
- Cervical curve
- C7
- T1
- Vertebrae
- Thoracic curve
- Intervertebral discs
- T12
- L1
- Intervertebral foramina
- Lumbar curve
- L5
- Sacrum
- Pelvic curve
- Coccyx

Figure 4-12. Vertebral column of an adult

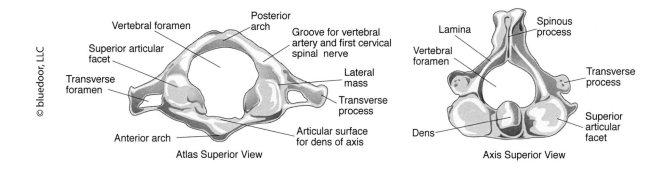

Figure 4-13. Cervical vertebrae 1 & 2: the atlas and the axis

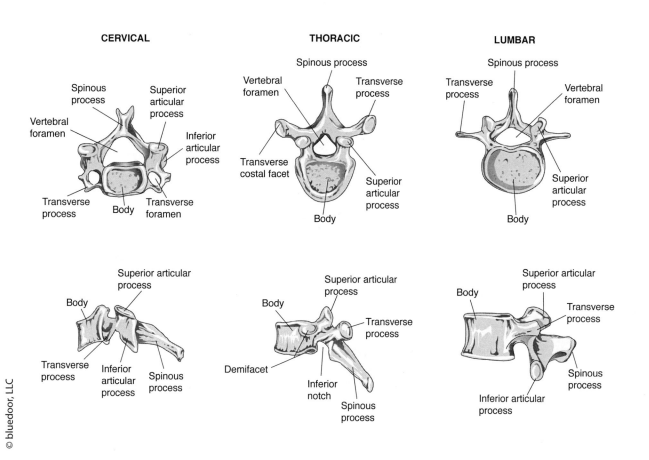

Figure 4-14. A comparison of vertebrae from the cervical, thoracic, and lumbar regions. Notice the difference in the shape and structures.

Sacrum and Coccyx Anterior and Posterior Views

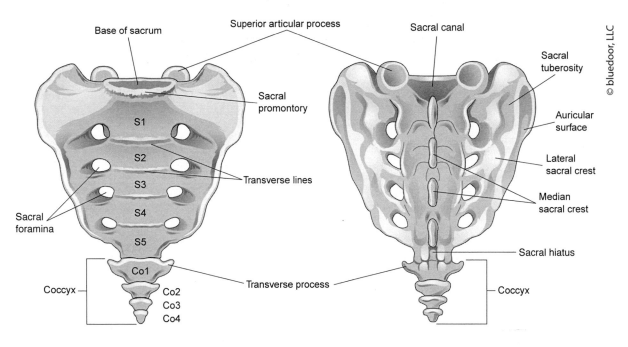

Figure 4-15. An anterior and posterior view of the sacrum and coccyx

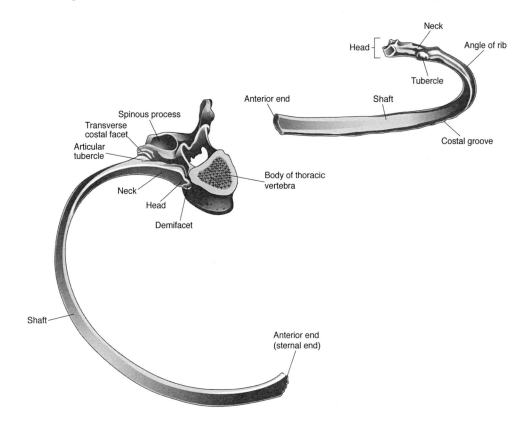

Figure 4-16. Sructures of a rib. Notice how the rib articulates with a vertebra in two places.

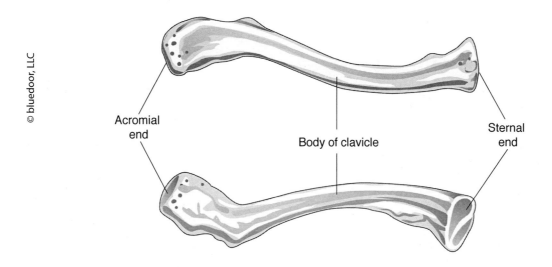

Acromial end

Body of clavicle

Sternal end

Figure 4-17. A superior and inferior view of a clavicle

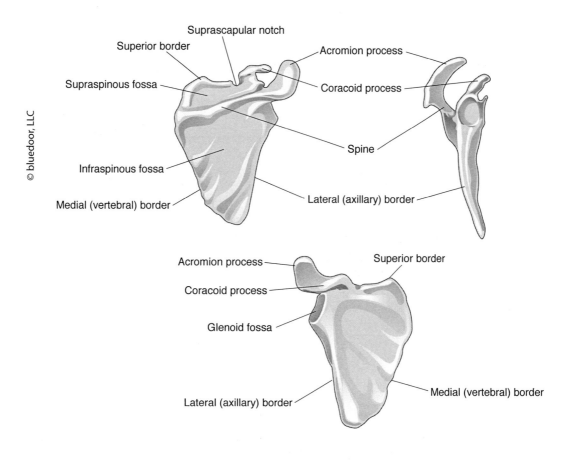

Suprascapular notch

Superior border

Acromion process

Supraspinous fossa

Coracoid process

Spine

Infraspinous fossa

Medial (vertebral) border

Lateral (axillary) border

Acromion process

Superior border

Coracoid process

Glenoid fossa

Lateral (axillary) border

Medial (vertebral) border

Figure 4-18. A posterior, lateral, and anterior view of a right scapula

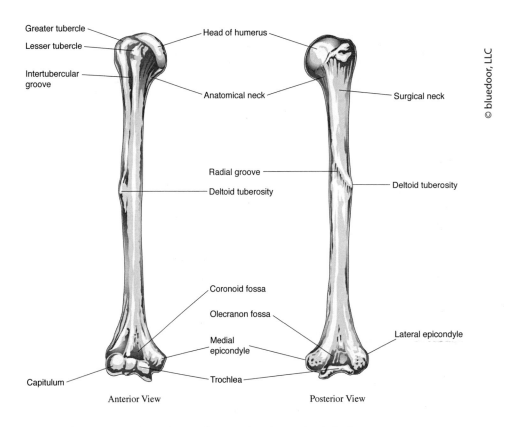

Figure 4-19. Anterior and posterior view of a right humerus

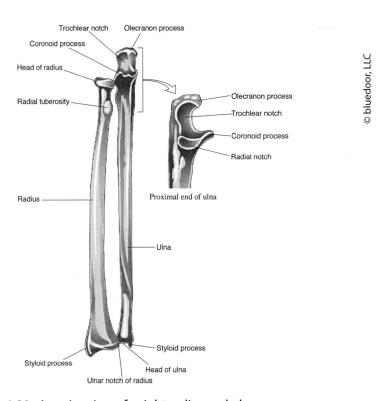

Figure 4-20. Anterior view of a right radius and ulna

© bluedoor, LLC

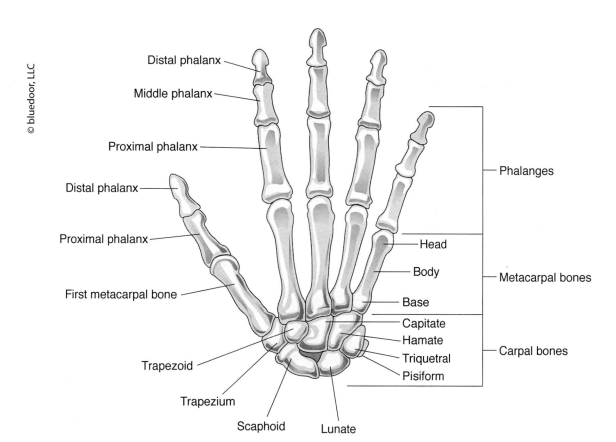

Distal phalanx

Middle phalanx

Proximal phalanx

Distal phalanx

Proximal phalanx

First metacarpal bone

Trapezoid

Trapezium

Scaphoid

Lunate

Phalanges

Head

Body

Base

Capitate

Hamate

Triquetral

Pisiform

Metacarpal bones

Carpal bones

Figure 4-21. Posterior view of a right hand

© bluedoor, LLC

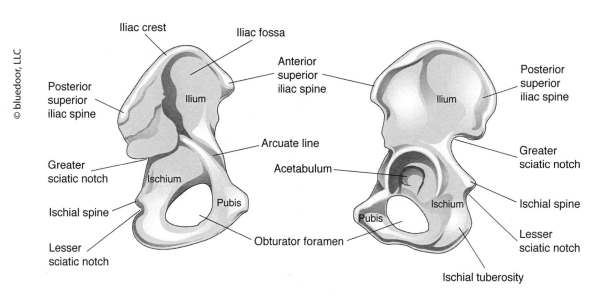

Iliac crest

Iliac fossa

Posterior
superior
iliac spine

Ilium

Anterior
superior
iliac spine

Greater
sciatic notch

Ischium

Arcuate line

Acetabulum

Pubis

Ischial spine

Lesser
sciatic notch

Obturator foramen

Ilium

Pubis

Ischium

Posterior
superior
iliac spine

Greater
sciatic notch

Ischial spine

Lesser
sciatic notch

Ischial tuberosity

Figure 4-22. A medial and lateral view of a left coxal bone

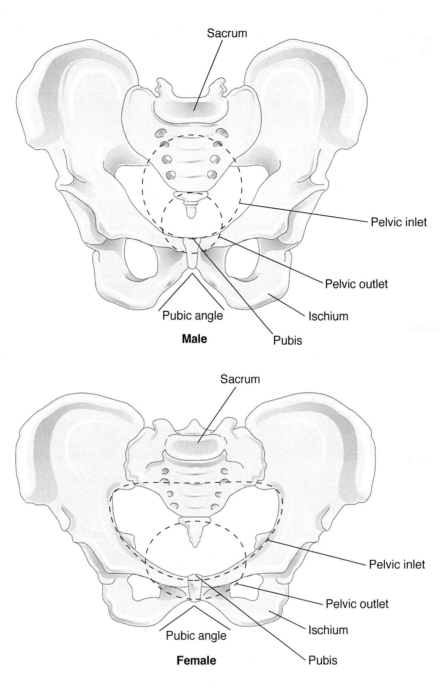

Figure 4-23. Comparison of a male and female pelvis

Right Femur, Anterior and Posterior Views

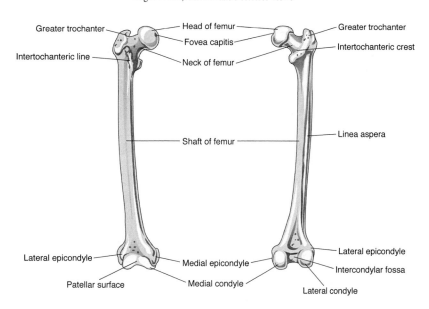

Greater trochanter

Intertochanteric line

Head of femur

Fovea capitis

Neck of femur

Greater trochanter

Intertochanteric crest

Shaft of femur

Linea aspera

Lateral epicondyle

Patellar surface

Medial epicondyle

Medial condyle

Lateral epicondyle

Intercondylar fossa

Lateral condyle

Figure 4-24. Anterior and posterior view of a right femur

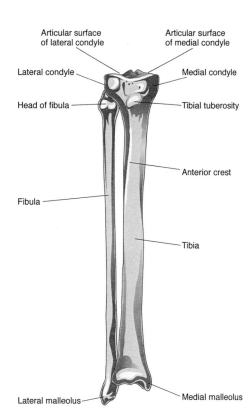

Articular surface
of lateral condyle

Lateral condyle

Head of fibula

Articular surface
of medial condyle

Medial condyle

Tibial tuberosity

Anterior crest

Fibula

Tibia

Lateral malleolus

Medial malleolus

Figure 4-25. Anterior view of right tibia and fibula

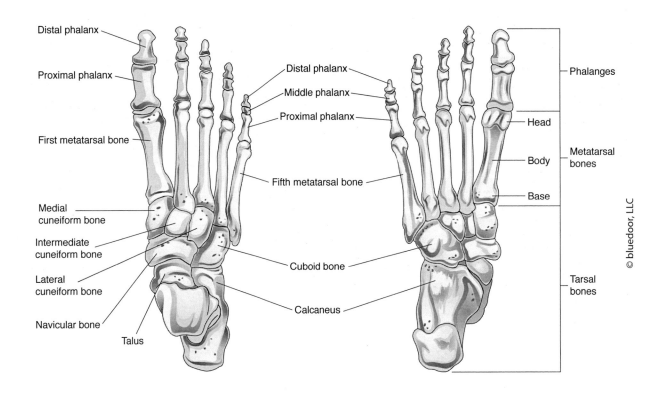

Distal phalanx

Proximal phalanx

First metatarsal bone

Medial cuneiform bone

Intermediate cuneiform bone

Lateral cuneiform bone

Navicular bone

Talus

Distal phalanx

Middle phalanx

Proximal phalanx

Fifth metatarsal bone

Cuboid bone

Calcaneus

Phalanges

Head

Metatarsal bones

Body

Base

Tarsal bones

Figure 4-26. Superior and inferior view of a right foot

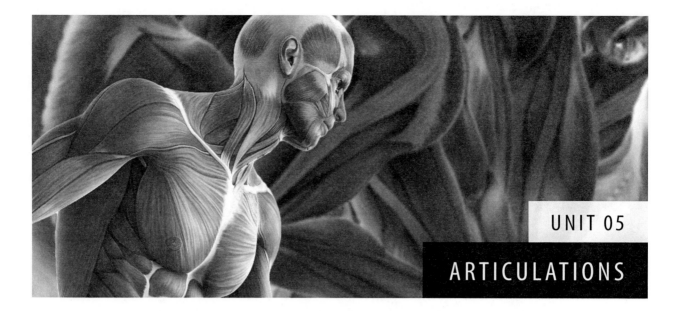

I. DEFINITION

An articulation or joint occurs wherever two or more bones come together and involves the articulating bones, the intervening material, and often supporting ligaments. It is helpful to differentiate between ligaments and tendons. Although both are typically composed of dense regular connective tissue, **ligaments** attach bones to bones, so form a prominent component of many articulations. In contrast, **tendons** attach muscle to bone or other structures on which they pull. Thus, they will feature more prominently in the following unit on muscles.

II. STRUCTURAL CLASSIFICATION

Articulations can be classified according to their structure or function. The structural classes (listed below) are based on the type of intervening tissue. Functional classes are based on the degree of movement permitted at the joint. There are three functional joint classes, including **synarthroses** (syn = together, arthro = joint), which permit virtually no movement (examples = sutures); **amphiarthroses** (amphi = both sides) which allow limited movement (example = pubic symphysis and intervertebral joints); and **diarthroses**, which are freely moveable (example = knee and shoulder). Know the following structural classes of joints. Further, know the degree of mobility allowed at each, and be familiar with multiple examples of where they are found. Given an articulation, you will be expected to be able to classify it as one of the following structural classes and know its degree of mobility:

A. Fibrous joint - bones joined by dense fibrous connective tissue. These are mostly synarthroses, with some exceptions.
  1. suture - joint formed by the articulation of bones of the skull, in adult no movement permitted
  2. syndesmosis(es) - longer bands of fibers, called **ligaments** or **interosseous membranes**, typically join the articulating bones (typically amphiarthrotic)
  3. gomphosis(es) - ligaments attach teeth to the alveolar sockets of the mandible and maxilla

B. Cartilaginous joint - bones held together by cartilage. These are either synarthrotic or amphiarthrotic.
   1. synchondrosis(es) - hyaline cartilage is intervening material
   2. symphysis(es) - fibrocartilage is intervening material

C. Synovial joint - fluid filled joint cavity, are all diarthrotic, and have the following basic components:
   1. articular cartilage (usually hyaline)
   2. joint cavity - space filled with synovial fluid
   3. articular capsule - outer fibrous, inner synovial membrane
   4. synovial fluid - ultra filtered blood plasma that lubricates surfaces
   5. reinforcing ligaments- dense regular connective tissue that connects the articulating bones
      a. intrinsic (capsular, no examples you need to know)
      b. intracapsular (example: cruciate ligaments of the knee)
      c. extracapsular (example: collateral ligaments of the knee)

6. Knee joint - the classic example of a synovial joint is the knee. Be able to identify the following structures on models and specimens available in the lab:
   lateral meniscus
   medial meniscus
   articular cartilage
   anterior cruciate ligament
   posterior cruciate ligament
   fibular (lateral) collateral ligament
   tibial (medial) collateral ligament
   patellar ligament
   tendon of quadriceps femoris

Give examples of the different types of articulations. To assist your study, fill in the table below:

Type	Definition	Example	Mobility
Suture			
Syndesmosis			
Gomphosis			
Synchondrosis			
Symphysis	2 or more bones held together by fibrocartilage	pubic symphysis	amphiarthrotic
Synovial			

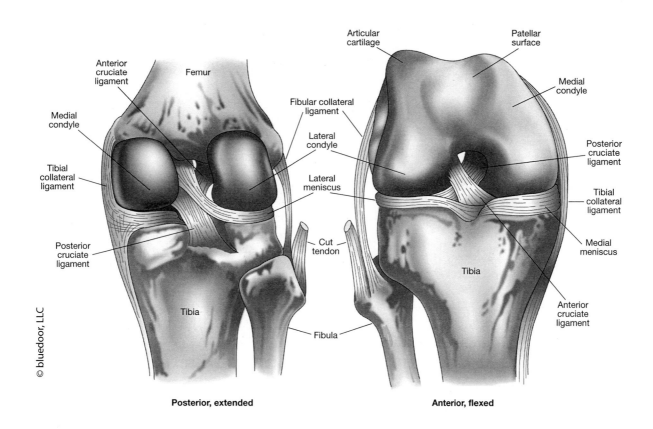

© bluedoor, LLC

Posterior, extended

Anterior, flexed

Anterior cruciate ligament

Femur

Medial condyle

Tibial collateral ligament

Posterior cruciate ligament

Tibia

Fibular collateral ligament

Lateral condyle

Lateral meniscus

Cut tendon

Fibula

Articular cartilage

Patellar surface

Medial condyle

Posterior cruciate ligament

Tibial collateral ligament

Medial meniscus

Anterior cruciate ligament

Tibia

Figure 5-1. Knee joint

ARTICULATIONS STUDY QUESTIONS

1. Teeth are peg-in-socket joints, also known as a _____ joints.

2. The pubic symphysis is comprised of what type of cartilage?

3. Name the 3 ligaments that attach on the femur and the tibia.

    A. _____

    B. _____

    C. _____

4. Name 2 extracapsular ligaments found in the knee joint.

    A. _____

    B. _____

5. Give 2 examples of suture joints in the body.

    A. _____

    B. _____

6. What is the difference between a tendon and a ligament?

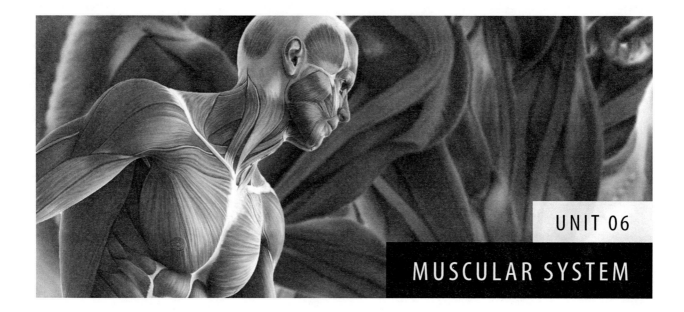

MUSCULAR SYSTEM

I. MICROSCOPIC ANATOMY

Three types of muscle tissue are found in the human body: **skeletal**, **cardiac**, and **smooth**. These muscle types exhibit differences in microscopic structure, body location, and function. The purpose of this exercise is to:

1. be able to distinguish the microscopic appearance of the different muscle types on slides and figures
2. know, in general, where the different muscle types are located
3. know, in general, the function of each muscle type
4. be able to distinguish the different muscle types based on characteristics

You should be able to distinguish between the 3 types of muscle tissue on slides, in figures, and by characteristic.

A. Skeletal Muscle (Striated Muscle)

1. location and function

Skeletal muscles originate and insert onto bones and occasionally skin or other muscles. Their primary functions are involved in voluntary movements e.g., locomotion, manipulation of the environment and facial expression.

2. microscopic structure

a. Skeletal muscles are composed of bundles (fascicles) of many muscle fibers (muscle cell = muscle fiber). These fascicles are enclosed in a connective tissue covering called the **perimysium**. Each muscle fiber is surrounded by a delicate layer of connective tissue called the **endomysium**. The connective tissue sheath surrounding the entire muscle is called the **epimysium**.

Use the space below to draw and label a cross section of a skeletal muscle, including fascicles, muscle fibers, and connective tissues.

Muscle fibers are very long, cylindrical, **multinucleated** cells. These cells exhibit a characteristic banding pattern, hence the term striated muscle. These striations correspond to the lines and bands of the sarcomere, the contractile unit of skeletal muscle.

Draw a single skeletal muscle fiber, labeling as many characteristics as possible.

B. Cardiac muscle

1. location and function

   Cardiac muscle is found only in the ventricular and atrial walls of the heart. Contraction of the cardiac muscle cells ultimately results in the contraction of the heart chambers, propelling blood into the arterial system. Regulation of contraction is involuntary, although the rate of contraction is under autonomic nervous system control.

2. microscopic structure

   Cardiac muscle consists of long, striated, cylindrical cells which branch (unlike skeletal and smooth muscle). The area where the individual cardiac muscle cells communicate with one another is called the **intercalated disc**. Notice that these cells are usually **uninucleated**, or occasionally binucleated, and that the nuclei are more centrally located within the cell compared to skeletal muscle.

Draw a few cardiac muscle cells, labeling as many characteristics as possible.

C. Smooth muscle
    1.   location and function

        Smooth muscle is located in the walls of hollow visceral organs, skin, portions of the respiratory tract, and in the walls of veins and arteries. When smooth muscle contracts it generally serves to propel (circulatory system) or churn (digestive system) contents along an internal tract. Control of smooth muscle is involuntary.

    2.   microscopic structure

        The microscopic appearance of smooth muscle is very different from skeletal or cardiac muscle. The uninucleated cells are long and spindle shaped, with **no striations**. They are often arranged in sheets or layers that run at right angles to one another.

Draw several smooth muscle cells, labeling as many characteristics as possible.

Skeletal Muscle Tissue

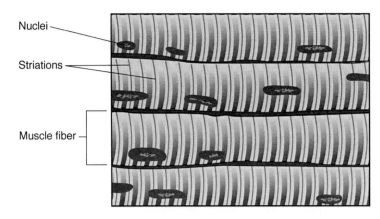

Nuclei

Striations

Muscle fiber

Figure 6-1. Microscopic anatomy of skeletal muscle

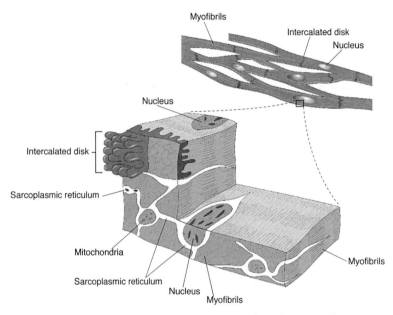

Myofibrils

Intercalated disk

Nucleus

Nucleus

Intercalated disk

Sarcoplasmic reticulum

Mitochondria

Sarcoplasmic reticulum

Nucleus

Myofibrils

Myofibrils

Figure 6-2. Microscopic anatomy of cardiac muscle

Smooth Muscle Tissue

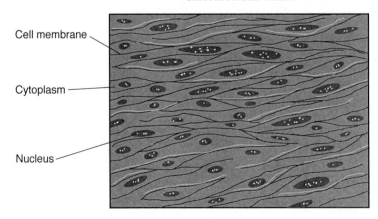

Cell membrane

Cytoplasm

Nucleus

Figure 6-3. Microscopic anatomy of smooth muscle

II. TERMINOLOGY

A. Muscle characteristics - using your textbook, complete the following table:

Term	Definition
Origin	
Insertion	
Tendon	collagen band that connects muscle to the skeleton
Aponeurosis	
Raphe	
Flexor	
Extensor	
Abductor	
Adductor	
Prime mover	
Synergist	
Fixator	type of synergist, prevents movement of a joint so that the origin of a prime mover is stabilized
Antagonist	

B. Types of movements - using your textbook, complete the following table:

Term	Definition
Flexion	
Extension	
Abduction	
Adduction	

Medial rotation	turn medially (i.e. arm, leg)
Lateral rotation	turn laterally
Circumduction	
Dorsiflexion	
Plantar flexion	
Inversion	
Eversion	
Protraction	
Retraction	
Elevation	
Depression	
Supination	
Pronation	
Opposition	
Reposition	

III. MUSCLES OF THE BODY

Be able to identify the following muscles of the body on a cadaver, model, or diagram. Not all of the following muscles will be demonstrated on the cadaver. Be sure to check with your TA regarding which muscles are demonstrated on the cadaver.

You are required to learn the origin, insertion, and action of all muscles marked with a double asterisk (**). You will be tested on this material. Please refer to the tables at the end of this section for muscle origins, insertions, and actions.

*Study tip: the name of the muscle will often reveal the origin, insertion and/or action.

A. Muscles of facial expression:
frontalis
orbicularis oculi
orbicularis oris
platysma
zygomaticus major
zygomaticus minor

B. Muscles of mastication:
masseter**
temporalis**

C. Extrinsic muscles of the tongue (floor of the oral cavity):
genioglossus
geniohyoid

D. Muscles of the neck:
  1. suprahyoid muscles (superior to the hyoid bone)
    digastric
      - anterior belly
      - posterior belly
    mylohyoid
    stylohyoid
  2. infrahyoid muscles (inferior to the hyoid bone)
    sternohyoid
    sternothyroid
    thyrohyoid
    omohyoid
      - superior belly
      - inferior belly
    sternocleidomastoid**
    anterior scalene **
    middle scalene **
    posterior scalene **

E. Muscles of the anterior thoracic wall:

pectoralis major**
pectoralis minor**
serratus anterior**
external intercostals**
internal intercostals**

F. Muscles of the anterior and lateral abdominal wall:
external oblique**
internal oblique**
rectus abdominis**
transversus abdominis

G. Muscles of the posterior abdominal wall:
iliacus**
psoas major**
quadratus lumborum

H. Muscles associated with the anterior compartment of the arm:
deltoid**
biceps brachii**
    - long head**
    - short head**
brachialis**
coracobrachialis**

I. Muscles associated with the posterior compartment of the forearm (note that the
    tendons of most of these muscles are supported distally by the extensor retinaculum):
brachioradialis**
extensor carpi radialis longus**
extensor carpi radialis brevis**
abductor pollicis longus**
extensor pollicis brevis**
extensor pollicis longus**
extensor digitorum**
extensor digiti minimi**
extensor indicis**
extensor carpi ulnaris**
supinator**
anconeus

J. Muscles associated with the anterior compartment of the thigh:
sartorius**
tensor fasciae lata(e)** - note that the iliotibial tract or band is a thick sheet of connective
    tissue that continues inferiorly from the tensor fasciae latae to the tibia and helps
    support the quadriceps femoris.
iliopsoas**
    (Iliacus and psoas major comprise the iliopsoas. They are located posterior to the
    abdominal cavity, and sometimes are not visible until after the abdominopelvic
    cavity is open.)
pectineus**
quadriceps femoris
    - rectus femoris**
    - vastus lateralis**
    - vastus medialis**
    - vastus intermedius**

K. Muscles associated with the medial compartment of the thigh:
gracilis**
adductor longus**
adductor brevis**
adductor magnus**

L. Muscles associated with the anterior compartment of the leg (note that the tendons of
    these muscles are secured distally by the superior and inferior extensor retinaculum):
tibialis anterior**
extensor hallucis longus**
extensor digitorum longus**
fibularis (peroneus) tertius**

M. Muscles associated with the lateral compartment of the leg
fibularis (peroneus) longus**
fibularis (peroneus) brevis**

N. Muscles associated with the posterior thoracic wall:
  1. pectoral girdle
  trapezius**
  levator scapula**
  rhomboid major**
  rhomboid minor**
  latissimus dorsi**

O. Muscles associated with the scapula:
supraspinatus**
infraspinatus**
teres major**
teres minor**
subscapularis**
The rotator cuff is comprised of four of the above muscles (remember them as the SITS muscles):
  1. supraspinatus S
  2. infraspinatus I
  3. teres minor   T
  4. subscapularis S

Look at these four muscles on a model or cadaver and explain below how they are important stabilizers of the shoulder joint.

P. Intrinsic muscles of the neck and back:
splenius capitis **
semispinalis capitis **
erector spinae
  - iliocostalis **
  - longissimus **
  - spinalis **

Q. Muscles associated with the posterior compartment of the arm:
triceps brachii
  - long head**
  - lateral head**
  - medial head**

R. Muscles associated with the anterior compartment of the forearm: (note that the tendons of many of these muscles are supported distally by the flexor retinaculum):
flexor carpi radialis**
palmaris longus**
flexor carpi ulnaris**
flexor digitorum superficialis**
flexor digitorum profundus**
flexor pollicis longus**
pronator quadratus **
pronator teres**

S. Intrinsic muscles of the hand:
abductor pollicis brevis**
opponens pollicis**
flexor pollicis brevis**
adductor pollicis**
abductor digiti minimi
flexor digiti minimi brevis
lumbricals
dorsal interossei

T. Muscles associated with the gluteal region and posterior compartment of the thigh:

1. gluteal region
gluteus maximus**
gluteus medius**
gluteus minimus**
piriformis**
quadratus femoris**
2. posterior compartment of the thigh
biceps femoris
- long head**
- short head**
semitendinosus**
semimembranosus**

U. Muscles associated with the posterior compartment of the leg (note that the gastrocnemius and soleus are anchored to the calcaneus by the calcaneal tendon):

gastrocnemius**
soleus**
tibialis posterior**
flexor digitorum longus**
flexor hallucis longus**

V. Intrinsic muscles of the foot:
extensor digitorum brevis
extensor hallucis brevis
abductor hallucis
abductor digiti minimi
flexor digitorum brevis

W. Muscles of the pelvic floor and perineum (identify on figures and models):
bulbospongiosus
coccygeus
ischiocavernosus
levator ani
deep transverse perineus
superficial transverse perineus

MUSCULAR SYSTEM STUDY QUESTIONS

1. Each skeletal muscle fiber is surrounded by delicate layer of connective tissue called the
_____.

2. TRUE or FALSE: Skeletal muscle fibers are uninucleated cells.

3. List all the actions at the hip joint during the motion involved with kicking a soccer ball.

4. Name 2 antagonists to tensor fasciae latae.

   A. _____

   B. _____

5. Which of the following muscles is a synergist to the biceps femoris long head?

   A. semitendinosus

   B. gluteus medius

   C. pectineus

   D. vastus lateralis

   E. gluteus minimis

6. Name 2 actions common to both the deltoid and latissimus dorsi.

   A. _____

   B. _____

7. TRUE or FALSE: Both the brachioradialis and the extensor carpi radialis longus insert on the the lateral supracondylar ridge of the humerus.

8. Lateral rotation of the radius that causes the palm to face anteriorly is called

   _____

9. Name 2 muscles that insert on the mastoid process.

   A. _____

   B. _____

10. Name the 4 the muscles that comprise the rotator cuff.

    A. _____

    B. _____

    C. _____

    D. _____

11. Which of the following muscles dorsiflexes the foot at the ankle and everts the foot?

    A. fibularis (peroneus) longus

    B. tibialis anterior

    C. fibularis (peroneus) brevis

    D. fibularis (peroneus) tertius

    E. tibialis posterior

12. TRUE or FALSE: Cardiac muscle tissue is found only in ventricular walls of the heart.

© bluedoor, LLC

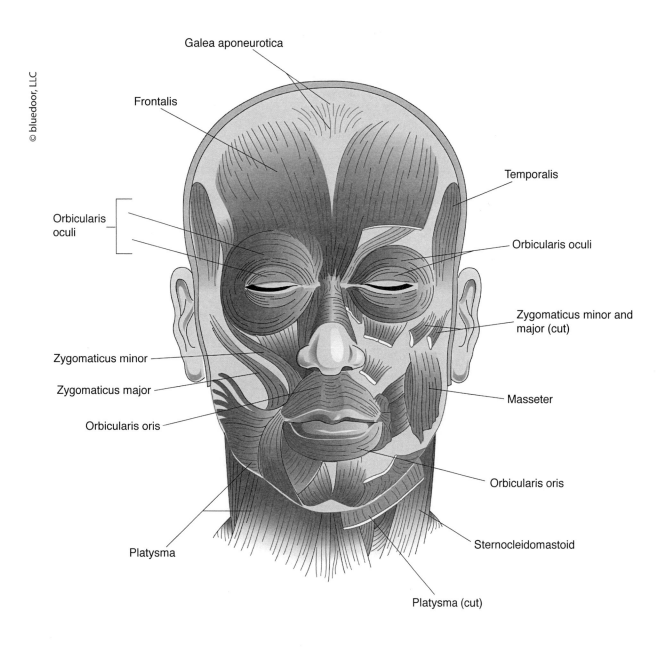

Galea aponeurotica

Frontalis

Orbicularis
oculi

Temporalis

Orbicularis oculi

Zygomaticus minor and
major (cut)

Zygomaticus minor

Zygomaticus major

Orbicularis oris

Masseter

Orbicularis oris

Platysma

Sternocleidomastoid

Platysma (cut)

Figure 6-4. Superficial facial muscles, anterior view.

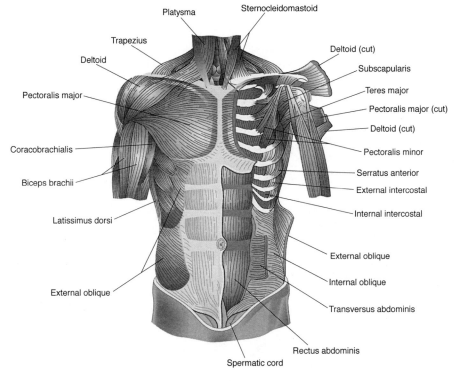

Figure 6-5. Anterior muscles of the torso

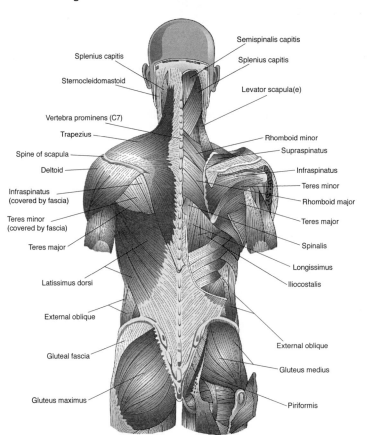

Figure 6-6. Posterior muscles of the torso

© bluedoor, LLC

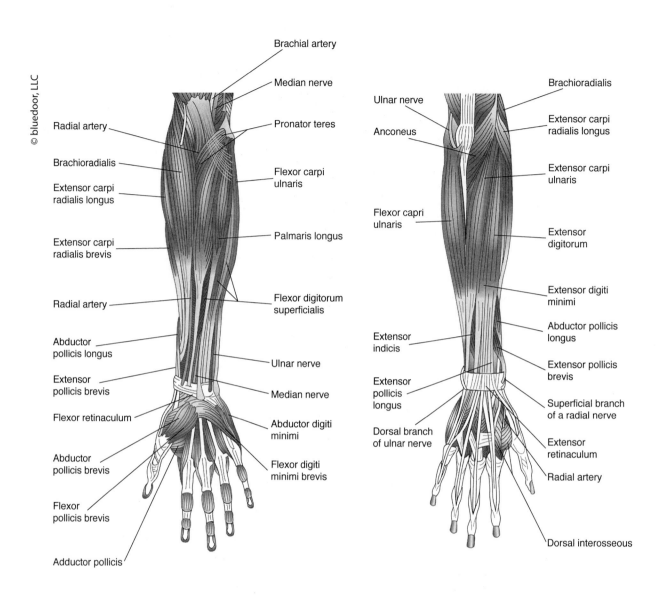

Brachial artery

Median nerve

Pronator teres

Flexor carpi
ulnaris

Palmaris longus

Flexor digitorum
superficialis

Ulnar nerve

Median nerve

Abductor digiti
minimi

Flexor digiti
minimi brevis

Radial artery

Brachioradialis

Extensor carpi
radialis longus

Extensor carpi
radialis brevis

Radial artery

Abductor
pollicis longus

Extensor
pollicis brevis

Flexor retinaculum

Abductor
pollicis brevis

Flexor
pollicis brevis

Adductor pollicis

Ulnar nerve

Anconeus

Flexor capri
ulnaris

Extensor
indicis

Extensor
pollicis
longus

Dorsal branch
of ulnar nerve

Brachioradialis

Extensor carpi
radialis longus

Extensor carpi
ulnaris

Extensor
digitorum

Extensor digiti
minimi

Abductor pollicis
longus

Extensor pollicis
brevis

Superficial branch
of a radial nerve

Extensor
retinaculum

Radial artery

Dorsal interosseous

Figure 6-7. Anterior and posterior muscles of the right forearm

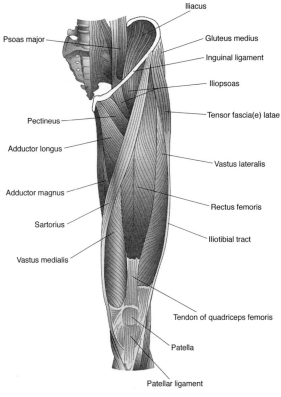

Figure 6-8. Anterior muscles of left thigh

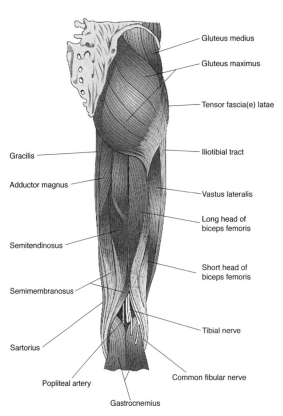

Figure 6-9. Posterior muscles of right thigh

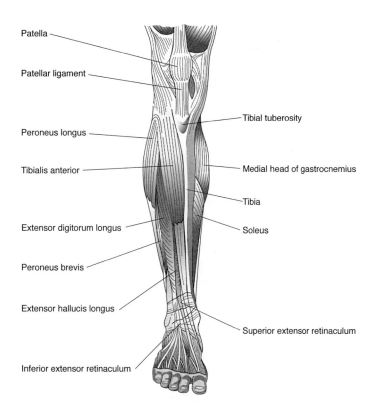

Patella

Patellar ligament

Peroneus longus

Tibialis anterior

Extensor digitorum longus

Peroneus brevis

Extensor hallucis longus

Inferior extensor retinaculum

Tibial tuberosity

Medial head of gastrocnemius

Tibia

Soleus

Superior extensor retinaculum

Figure 6-10. Anterior muscles of right leg

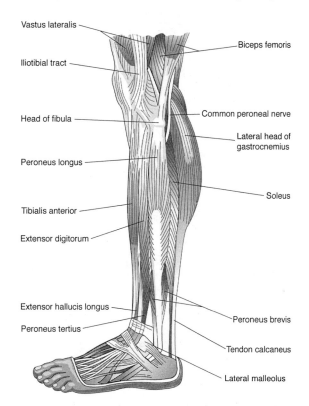

Vastus lateralis

Iliotibial tract

Head of fibula

Peroneus longus

Tibialis anterior

Extensor digitorum

Extensor hallucis longus

Peroneus tertius

Biceps femoris

Common peroneal nerve

Lateral head of gastrocnemius

Soleus

Peroneus brevis

Tendon calcaneus

Lateral malleolus

Figure 6-11. Lateral view of muscles of left leg

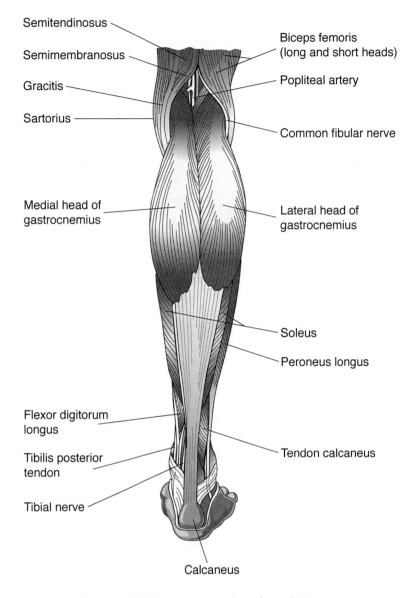

Semitendinosus

Semimembranosus

Gracitis

Sartorius

Biceps femoris
(long and short heads)

Popliteal artery

Common fibular nerve

Medial head of
gastrocnemius

Lateral head of
gastrocnemius

Soleus

Peroneus longus

Flexor digitorum
longus

Tibilis posterior
tendon

Tibial nerve

Tendon calcaneus

Calcaneus

Figure 6-12. Posterior muscles of a right leg

© bluedoor, LLC

TABLES FOR MUSCLE ORIGINS, INSERTIONS, AND ACTIONS

The level of detail at which you need to know the muscle origins, insertions, and actions appears in these tables. Note that the information is organized differently from the way it appears in the preceding pages of your lab manual. These tables are organized according to muscular location or functional grouping.

Some thoughts and hints on the best way to learn muscle actions.
    One of the best ways is to organize by action over a particular body area.
    For example:
        Muscles that move the humerus (and therefore must, in part, insert on the humerus)
           <u>Arm adductors</u>
           pectoralis major
           latissimus dorsi
           teres major

           <u>Arm abductors</u>
           deltoid
           supraspinatus

You can continue this exercise yourself. Some suggestions:
1. List the movements possible over a joint
2. Fill in the muscles that perform that particular movement.
3. When learning origins and insertions, picture the muscle contracting and shortening, it helps to make the action more understandable
4. Review the ways in which muscles are named. You will notice that often times the origin, insertion, or action are used to name the muscle; and (hallelujah !), sometimes two or more of these things (e.g., sternocleidomastoid).
5. For the limbs, here are some general rules:

    <u>Upper limb</u> -   muscles located in the anterior compartment are flexors
                      muscles located in the posterior compartment are extensors

    <u>Lower limb</u> -   muscles located in the anterior compartment are extensors
                      muscles located in the posterior compartment are flexors

6. To help you learn muscle actions, picture the muscle from its origin to its insertion and look at how as it passes over the joint. Visualize the muscle contracting and how this would move the joint.
7. Make use of your own body. Try and isolate a muscle, and feel it as it moves.

MUSCLES OF MASTICATION

Muscle	Origin	Insertion	Action
masseter	zygomatic arch	mandibular angle and mandibular ramus	elevates mandible
temporalis	temporal fossa of the temporal bone	coronoid process of the mandible	elevates mandible, and retracts mandible

MUSCLES OF THE NECK

Muscle	Origin	Insertion	Action
sternocleidomastoid	manubrium, medial clavicle	mastoid process of the temporal bone	flexes and rotates the head
scalenes anterior, middle, posterior	transverse processes of the cervical vertebrae	anterior surface of ribs 1-2	elevates ribs 1-2, flexes neck, rotates neck

MUSCLES OF THE ANTERIOR THORACIC WALL

Muscle	Origin	Insertion	Action
pectoralis major	sternal end of the clavicle, sternum, ribs 1-6	greater tubercle of the humerus	flexes arm at shoulder, rotates arm medially, adducts arm
pectoralis minor	ribs 3-5	coracoid process of the scapula	depresses scapula, rotates scapula downwards
serratus anterior	ribs 1-8	vertebral border of the scapula	rotates scapula upwards, protracts scapula
external intercostals	inferior border of ribs	superior border of ribs	elevates rib cage
internal intercostals	superior border of ribs	inferior border of ribs	depresses rib cage

MUSCLES OF THE ANTERIOR AND LATERAL ABDOMEN WALL

Muscle	Origin	Insertion	Action
external oblique	ribs 5-12	linea alba, pubic crest, pubic tubercle, iliac crest	flexes and rotates vertebral column, compresses abdomen
internal oblique	lumbar fascia, iliac crest, inguinal ligament	linea alba, pubic crest, ribs 9-12	flexes and rotates vertebral column, compresses abdomen
rectus abdominis	pubic crest, pubic symphysis	xiphoid process of the sternum, ribs 5-7	flexes and rotates vertebral column, compresses abdomen

MUSCLES OF THE POSTERIOR ABDOMINAL WALL

Muscle	Origin	Insertion	Action
iliacus	iliac fossa, ala of the sacrum	lesser trochanter of the femur	flexes thigh at hip, flexes trunk
psoas major	transverse processes of T12-L5	lesser trochanter of the femur	flexes thigh at hip, flexes trunk laterally

MUSCLES OF THE ANTERIOR COMPARTMENT OF THE ARM

Muscle	Origin	Insertion	Action
deltoid	lateral 1/3 of clavicle, spine of scapula, acromion process of the scapula	deltoid tuberosity of the humerus	abducts arm; flexes arm at shoulder, rotates arm medially, extends arm at shoulder, rotates arm laterally
biceps brachii long head	supraglenoid tubercle of the scapula	radial tuberosity	flexes forearm at elbow, supinates forearm
short head	coracoid process of the scapula	radial tuberosity	flexes forearm at elbow, supinates forearm
brachialis	anterior humerus	coronoid process of the ulna	flexes forearm at elbow
coracobrachialis	coracoid process	medial surface of shaft of humerus	flexes arm at shoulder, adducts arm

MUSCLES OF THE POSTERIOR COMPARTMENT OF THE FOREARM

Muscle	Origin	Insertion	Action
brachioradialis	lateral supracondylar ridge of the humerus	styloid process of the radius	flexes forearm at elbow, stabilizes elbow during flexion and extension
extensor carpi radialis longus	lateral supracondylar ridge of the humerus	2nd metacarpal	extends hand at wrist, abducts hand
extensor carpi radialis brevis	lateral epicondyle of the humerus	3rd metacarpal	extends hand at wrist, abducts hand
extensor digitorum	lateral epicondyle of the humerus	distal phalanges of 2nd to 5th digit	extends distal interphalangeal joints, extends hand at wrist
extensor carpi ulnaris	lateral epicondyle of the humerus, posterior ulna	5th metacarpal	extends hand at wrist, adducts hand
supinator	lateral epicondyle of the humerus, proximal ulna	proximal end of radius	supinates forearm
abductor pollicis longus	posterior radius, posterior ulna, interosseous membrane	trapezium, 1st metacarpal	abducts pollex
extensor pollicis brevis	posterior radius, posterior ulna, interosseous membrane	proximal phalanx of pollex	extends 1st metacarpal-phalangeal joint
extensor pollicis longus	posterior radius, posterior ulna, interosseous membrane	distal phalanx pollex	extends 1st interphalangeal joint
extensor indicis	posterior ulna, interosseous membrane	distal phalanx of 2nd digit	extends 2nd distal interphalangeal joint
extensor digiti minimi	lateral epicondyle of the humerus	distal phalanx of 5th digit	extends 5th distal interphalangeal joint

MUSCLES ASSOCIATED WITH THE ANTERIOR COMPARTMENT OF THE THIGH

Muscle	Origin	Insertion	Action
sartorius	anterior superior iliac spine	medial surface of proximal tibia	flexes thigh at hip, rotates thigh laterally, abducts thigh, flexes leg at knee
tensor fascia(e) latae	anterior superior iliac spine, iliac crest	iliotibial tract	flexes thigh at hip, abducts thigh, rotates thigh medially
iliopsoas	iliac fossa, ala of the sacrum, transverse processes of T12-L5	lesser trochanter of the femur	flexes thigh at hip, flexes vertebral column
pectineus	superior ramus of the pubis	linea aspera	adducts thigh, flexes thigh at hip, rotates thigh medially
quadriceps femoris rectus femoris	anterior inferior iliac spine	all four: patella and tibial tuberosity via tendon of quadriceps femoris and patellar ligament	extends leg at knee, flexes thigh at hip
vastus lateralis	greater trochanter, intertrochanteric line, linea aspera of the femur		extends leg at knee, stabilizes knee
vastus medialis	linea aspera, intertrochanteric line of the femur		extends leg at knee, stabilizes patella
vastus intermedius	proximal shaft of the femur		extends leg at knee

MUSCLES ASSOCIATED WITH THE MEDIAL COMPARTMENT OF THE THIGH

Muscle	Origin	Insertion	Action
gracilis	inferior ramus of the pubis, body of the pubis	medial surface of the tibia	adducts thigh, flexes leg at knee, rotates leg medially
adductor longus	pubis – near pubic symphysis	linea aspera of the femur	adducts thigh, flexes thigh at hip, rotates thigh medially
adductor brevis	body of the pubis, inferior ramus of the pubis	linea aspera, adductor tubercle	adducts thigh, rotates thigh medially
adductor magnus	inferior ramus of the pubis, ischial ramus, ischial tuberosity	linea aspera, adductor tubercle	adducts thigh, rotates thigh medially, flexes thigh at hip

MUSCLES ASSOCIATED WITH THE ANTERIOR COMPARTMENT OF THE LEG

Muscle	Origin	Insertion	Action
tibialis anterior	lateral condyle of the tibia, interosseous membrane	medial cuneiform, 1st metatarsal	dorsiflexes foot at ankle, inverts foot
extensor hallucis longus	proximal shaft of the fibula, interosseous membrane	distal phalanx of the great toe	dorsiflexes foot at ankle, extends great toe
extensor digitorum longus	lateral condyle of the tibia, proximal fibula, interosseous membrane	middle and distal phalanges of 2nd-5th digits	extends 2nd-5th distal interphalangeal joints
fibularis (peroneus) tertius	distal shaft of fibula, interosseous membrane	5th metatarsal	dorsiflexes foot at ankle, everts foot

MUSCLES ASSOCIATED WITH THE LATERAL COMPARTMENT OF THE LEG

Muscle	Origin	Insertion	Action
fibularis (peroneus) longus	head of the fibula	medial cuneiform, 1st metatarsal	plantar flexes foot at ankle, everts foot
fibularis (peroneus) brevis	distal shaft of fibula	5th metatarsal	plantar flexes foot at ankle, everts foot

MUSCLES OF THE POSTERIOR THORACIC WALL

Muscle	Origin	Insertion	Action
trapezius	occipital bone, spinous processes of C7-T12	lateral 1/3 of clavicle, spine of scapula, acromion process of the scapula	elevates scapula, depresses scapula, rotates scapula, adducts scapula
latissimus dorsi	spinous processes of T7-T12, ribs 9-12, iliac crest	intertubercular groove (sulcus) of the humerus	extends arm at shoulder, adducts arm, rotates arm medially
levator scapula(e)	transverse processes of C1-C4	vertebral border of the scapula	elevates scapula, downwardly rotates scapula
rhomboid major	spinous processes of T2-T5	vertebral border of the scapula	adducts scapula, downwardly rotates scapula
rhomboid minor	spinous processes of C7-T1	vertebral border of the scapula	adducts scapula, downwardly rotates scapula

MUSCLES ASSOCIATED WITH THE SCAPULA

Muscle	Origin	Insertion	Action
supraspinatus	supraspinous fossa of the scapula	greater tubercle of the humerus	abducts arm
infraspinatus	infraspinous fossa of the scapula	greater tubercle of the humerus	rotates arm laterally
teres major	inferior angle of the scapula	lesser tubercle of the humerus	adducts arm, extends arm at shoulder, rotates arm medially
teres minor	lateral border of the scapula	greater tubercle of the humerus	rotates arm laterally
subscapularis	subscapular fossa	lesser tubercle of the humerus	rotates arm medially

INTRINSIC MUSCLES OF THE NECK AND BACK

Muscle	Origin	Insertion	Action
splenius capitis	spinous processes of C6-T7	mastoid process of the temporal bone, occipital bone	extends vertebral column
semispinalis capitis	transverse processes of C7-T12	occipital bone	extends vertebral column
erector spinae iliocostalis	iliac crest, ribs 3-12	inferior border of the ribs, transverse processes of C4-C6	extends vertebral column
longissimus	transverse processes of C4-L5	mastoid process of the temporal bone	extends vertebral column
spinalis	spinous processes of T7-L3	spinous processes of C4-T6	extends vertebral column

MUSCLES OF THE POSTERIOR COMPARTMENT OF THE ARM

Muscle	Origin	Insertion	Action
triceps brachii long head	infraglenoid tubercle of the scapula	olecranon process of the ulna	extends forearm at elbow
lateral head	posterior surface of shaft of humerus	olecranon process of the ulna	extends forearm at elbow
medial head	posterior surface of shaft of humerus	olecranon process of the ulna	extends forearm at elbow

MUSCLES OF THE ANTERIOR COMPARTMENT OF THE FOREARM

Muscle	Origin	Insertion	Action
flexor carpi radialis	medial epicondyle of the humerus	2nd and 3rd metacarpals	flexes hand at wrist, abducts hand
palmaris longus	medial epicondyle of the humerus	palmar aponeurosis	flexes hand at wrist
flexor carpi ulnaris	medial epicondyle of the humerus, olecaranon process of the ulna, shaft of the ulna	pisiform, hamate, 5th metacarpal	flexes hand at wrist, adducts hand
flexor digitorum superficialis	medial epicondyle of the humerus, coronoid process of ulna, shaft of radius	middle phalanges of 2nd to 5th digit	flexes hand at wrist, flexes proximal interphalangeal joints
flexor digitorum profundus	ulna and interosseus membrane	distal phalanges of 2nd to 5th digit	flexes distal interphalangeal joints
flexor pollicis longus	anterior radius and interosseus membrane	distal phalanx of pollex	flexes 1st interphalangeal joint
pronator quadratus	distal and anterior ulna	distal and anterior radius	pronates forearm
pronator teres	medial epicondyle of the humerus	lateral radius	pronates forearm

INTRINSIC MUSCLES OF THE HAND

Muscle	Origin	Insertion	Action
abductor pollicis brevis	scaphoid, trapezium, flexor retinaculum	proximal phalanx of thumb	abducts thumb
opponens pollicis	trapezium, flexor retinaculum	1st metacarpal	opposition
flexor pollicis brevis	trapezium, flexor retinaculum	proximal phalanx of pollex	flexes thumb
adductor pollicis	capitate, bases of 2nd-4th metacarpals	proximal phalanx of pollex	adducts thumb, opposition

MUSCLES ASSOCIATED WITH THE GLUTEAL REGION AND POSTERIOR COMPARTMENT OF THE THIGH			
Muscle	Origin	Insertion	Action
gluteus maximus	posterior surface of ala of ilium, sacrum, coccyx	iliotibial tract, gluteal tuberosity of the femur	extends thigh at hip, rotates thigh laterally, abducts thigh
gluteus medius	lateral surface of the ilium	greater trochanter of the femur	abducts thigh, rotates thigh medially
gluteus minimis	lateral surface of the ilium	greater trochanter of the femur	abducts thigh, rotates thigh medially
piriformis	lateral surface of the sacrum	greater trochanter of the femur	rotates thigh laterally when hip is extended
quadratus femoris	ischial tuberosity	intertrochanteric crest of the femur	rotates thigh laterally
biceps femoris long head	ischial tuberosity, linea aspera of the femur	head of the fibula, lateral condyle of the tibia	extends thigh at hip, flexes leg at knee, rotates leg laterally
short head	linea aspera of the femur	head of the fibula, lateral condyle of the tibia	flexes leg at knee, rotates leg laterally
semitendinosus	ischial tuberosity	medial surface of proximal shaft of tibia	extends thigh at hip, flexes leg at knee, rotates leg medially
semimembranosus	ischial tuberosity	medial condyle of the tibia	extends thigh at hip; flexes leg at knee, rotates leg medially

MUSCLES ASSOCIATED WITH THE POSTERIOR COMPARTMENT OF THE LEG			
Muscle	Origin	Insertion	Action
gastrocnemius	lateral condyle of the femur, medial condyle the femur	calcaneus	plantar flexes foot at ankle
soleus	proximal tibia, proximal fibula, interosseous membrane	calcaneus	plantar flexes foot at ankle
tibialis posterior	proximal tibia, proximal fibula, interosseous membrane	navicular bone, 2nd-4th metatarsal	plantar flexes foot at ankle, inverts foot
flexor digitorum longus	posterior shaft of tibia	distal phalanges of 2nd-5th digits	plantar flexes foot at ankle, inverts foot, flexes 2nd-5th distal interphalangeal joints
flexor hallucis longus	middle shaft of the fibula, interosseous membrane	distal phalanx of hallux	plantar flexes foot at ankle, inverts foot, flexes big toe

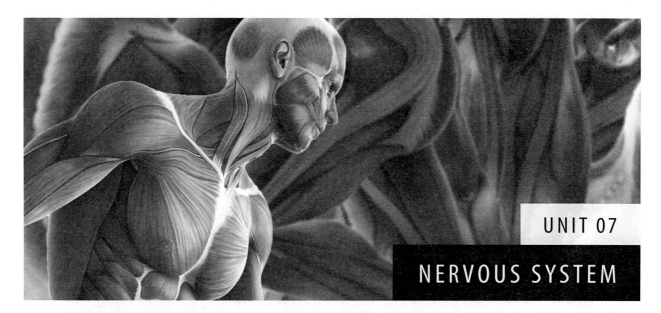

NERVOUS SYSTEM

I. CENTRAL NERVOUS SYSTEM (CNS)

A. Embryology – in order to understand the terminology applied to the divisions and structures of the adult CNS, it is helpful to have a basic understanding of how it develops. The CNS starts as a hollow tube, called the neural tube, running on the dorsal surface of the embryo. The brain develops from its rostral end, while the more caudal portions give rise to the spinal cord. At the rostral end of the neural tube, three primary vesicles develop as a result of its expansion and growth; these vesicles are the <u>prosencephalon</u>, <u>mesencephalon</u>, and the <u>rhombencephalon</u>. Continued growth gives rise to secondary vesicles (see table below). It is from these basic structures that the regions of the adult brain develop. Keep in mind that the tube is hollow, and, in the adult this hollow portion is retained as the <u>ventricular system.</u>

Please fill in the table below:

Primary Brain Vesicle	Secondary Brain Vesicle	Adult Brain Structure	Associated Ventricle or Canal of Adult
Prosencephalon (Forebrain)	Telencephalon		
	Diencephalon		3rd ventricle
Mesencephalon (Midbrain)	Mesencephalon	brain stem, midbrain	
Rhombencephalon (Hindbrain)	Metencephalon		
	Myelencephalon		

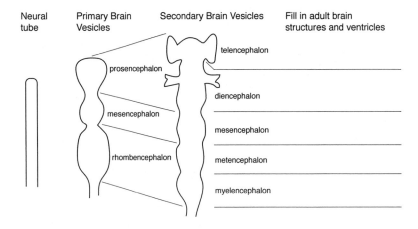

Neural tube   Primary Brain Vesicles   Secondary Brain Vesicles   Fill in adult brain structures and ventricles

prosencephalon

mesencephalon

rhombencephalon

telencephalon

diencephalon

mesencephalon

metencephalon

myelencephalon

B. Terminology – be able to define and appropriately use the following terms:

Term	Definition	Example
Cortex		
Gyrus (gyri)		
Sulcus (sulci)		
Fissure	deep depressions or inward folds of the brain	transverse fissure
Cerebral or cerebellar lobe		
White matter		
Gray matter		
Fiber tract (=association, commisural, & projection fibers)		
Nerve		
Nerve plexus		
Nucleus (within the CNS; **not** the same as within a cell)		
Ganglion		
Folia		

© bluedoor, LLC

C. Microscopic anatomy – there are 2 general types of cells in nervous tissue: neurons and glial cells. Both are found in both the CNS and PNS
  1. Neurons – these are the functional cells of the nervous system, generating and propagating electrical signals.
    a. Types - there are 3 types of neurons, based on what kind of information they carry.
      i. sensory
      ii. motor
      iii. interneurons
    b. Shapes – there are three types of neurons based on their shapes. You should know generally what kind of information is carried by each.
      i. unipolar
      ii. bipolar
      iii. multipolar
    b. Features – be able to identify the following features of a typical neuron on a figure or model:
      i. soma
      ii. axon
      iii. dendrites
      iv. Nissl bodies
      v. nodes of Ranvier
      vi. axon terminals

  2. Glia – these are the support cells of nervous tissue. They help ensure the environment around the neuron supports its function. There are 6 types of glial cells, 4 in the CNS and 2 in the PNS. Be able to differentiate the cell type based on location and function.
    a. CNS
      i. astrocytes
      ii. oligodendrocytes
      iii. ependymal cells
      iv. microglia
    b. PNS
      i. Schwann cells
      ii. satellite cells

D. Brain – be able to identify the following structures on a human brain, models and charts available in the lab. **Be sure to observe structures in different planes** (i.e. mid-sagittal view, dorsal view, and ventral view).
  1. cerebrum – right and left cerebral hemispheres
    a. gyri –
       precentral gyrus
       postcentral gyrus
    b. sulci –
       central sulcus
       lateral sulcus (Sylvian fissure)
       parieto-occipital sulcus
    c. fissures –
       longitudinal fissure
       transverse fissure
    d. lobes – be able to identify and state the boundaries of:

frontal lobes
    boundaries=
parietal lobes
    boundaries=
temporal lobes
    boundaries=
occipital lobes
    boundaries=
  e. fiber tracts –
     corpus callosum
     anterior commissure
     fornix
  f. lateral ventricle
     choroid plexus
     septum pellucidum
  g. olfactory bulbs & olfactory tracts

2. diencephalon – the diencephalon consists primarily of three <u>paired</u> structures, the thalamus, the hypothalamus, and the epithalamus. The hypothalamus and thalamus are both composed of many discrete nuclei, which are addressed in more detail in lecture.
  a. visual pathway components –
     optic chiasm
     optic nerves
     optic tract
  b. thalamus –
     intermediate mass (also called interthalamic adhesion)
     interventricular foramen (of Monroe)
     third ventricle
     choroid plexus
  c. hypothalamus –
     mammillary bodies
     infundibulum
     pituitary gland (hypophysis) - functionally separated into the anterior (adenohypophysis) and posterior (neurohypophysis) pituitary gland
  d. epithalamus –
     pineal gland
     posterior commissure
3. brain stem – consists of three different regions: midbrain, pons, medulla oblongata
  a. midbrain –
     cerebral peduncles
     posterior commissure
     cerebral aqueduct
     corpora quadrigemina (note that the region formed by the corpora quadrigemina is sometimes referred to as the tectum, which means "roof" in latin)
     superior colliculus (paired)
     inferior colliculus (paired)

What do the cerebral peduncles contain? (think function!)

    b. pons –
        fourth ventricle
        superior cerebellar peduncles
        middle cerebellar peduncles
        inferior cerebellar peduncles
    c. medulla oblongata –
        pyramids
        olive

4. cerebellum –
      cerebellar hemispheres
      vermis
      transverse fissure
      folia
      sulci
      arbor vitae
      middle cerebellar peduncles
      fourth ventricle

5. ventricular system – found within all regions of the brain
      lateral ventricles
      septum pellucidum
      choroid plexus
      interventricular foramen (of Monroe)
      cerebral aquaduct
      third ventricle
      fourth ventricle
      central canal

6. coverings and protection of the brain – the brain is protected from injury by three structures: 1) the cranium, 2) meninges, and 3) a fluid cushion.
    a. cranium – review the bones that form the cranium:
        frontal
        parietal
        temporal
        occipital

Also take some time to review the cranial fossae and observe which regions of the brain occupy the cranial fossae.

    b. meninges – the brain and spinal cord are covered by three layers of connective tissue collectively refered to as the meninges.
        dura mater
        arachnoid mater
        pia mater

i. The outer most layer, the **dura mater**, is a very tough double layered membrane. The outer surface adheres to the cranium and serves as the periosteal layer; the inner layer is the meningeal layer. The dura mater extends down into the longitudinal and transverse fissures as the **falx cerebri** and **tentorium cerebelli**, respectively. It also fomrs the **diaphragma sellae**, which holds the pineal gland in the sella turcica, and the **falx cerebelli**, with separates the right and left cerebellar hemispheres. Following the boundaries of the falx cerebri and tentorium cerebelli, and contained between the two layers of the dura mater, are dural sinuses. These are blood filled spaces, listed on page 100.

ii. The middle layer is the **arachnoid mater**. **Arachnoid villi** (also called arachnoid granulations) project into the dural sinuses, especially the superior sagittal sinus. CSF passes through the arachnoid villi from the sub arachnoid space to the venous blood.

iii. The inner most layer, the **pia mater**, is closely adherent to the surface of the brain.

Draw a cross section (showing the brain and cranium, if that helps) illustrating the three meningeal layers:

c. fluid cushion – cerebrospinal fluid (CSF) is a clear liquid containing glucose, proteins, cations, and ions. You should be able to explain:

    i. Where is CSF formed, and by what?

    ii. Be able to trace the circulation of CSF through the CNS (don't forget the spinal cord).

        lateral ventricles ————>

    iii. Through what structure(s) is CSF returned to the venous system?

        7. blood supply – be able to identify the following arteries of the brain.
            vertebral artery
            basilar artery
            posterior cerebral artery
            posterior communicating artery
            internal carotid artery
            middle cerebral artery
            anterior communicating artery
            anterior cerebral artery

    a. You should know, in general, which regions of the brain the following arteries supply:

Artery	Region Supplied
Anterior cerebral	
Middle cerebral	
Posterior cerebral	occipital lobe
Basilar	pons, medulla oblongata

    b. Which arteries contribute to the arterial circle of Willis?

What is functionally unique and/or important about the arterial circle of Willis?

8. venous drainage – the veins of the brain drain into various dural sinuses, which eventually drain into the internal jugular veins. Be able to:
a. Define what is meant by dural sinus.

b. Identify the following (check out the dura mater of the cadavers – you may see some nice examples of these!):
superior sagittal sinus
inferior sagittal sinus
straight sinus
transverse sinus
confluence of the sinuses

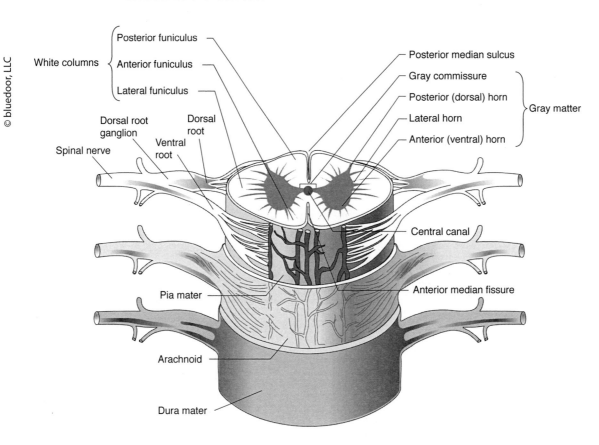

Figure 7-1. X-section of a spinal cord

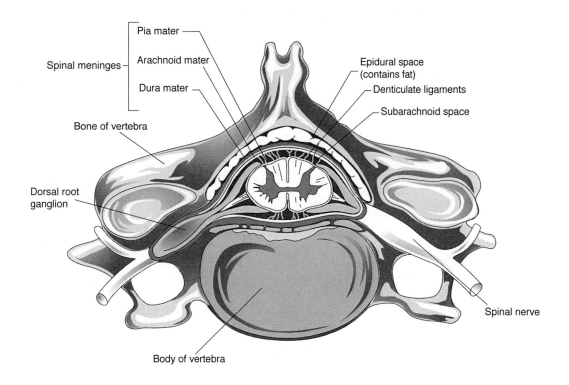

Figure 7-2. Spinal cord within the vertebral foramen of a cervical vertebra

E. Spinal cord – be able to identify the following structures:

1. general characteristics –

cervical enlargement
lumbar enlargement
conus medullaris
filum terminale
cauda equina
denticulate ligaments
spinal roots

a. Can you deduce why there is a cervical and lumbar enlargement in the spinal cord?

b. Lumbar punctures (to take a sample of CSF) are usually done between $L_3 - L_4$, or $L_4 - L_5$. Why do you think this is so?

c. What is the function of the filum terminale?

d. What is the cauda equina?

2. cross sectional anatomy (models only)
   a.   gray matter –
       anterior (ventral) horns
       posterior (dorsal) horns
       lateral horns
       gray commissure
       central canal
   b.   white matter –
       anterior column (funiculus)
       posterior column (funiculus)
       lateral column (funiculus)
       anterior median fissure
       posterior median sulcus
   c.   Be able to answer the following questions concerning the spinal cord:
       i.   Sensory input is received by which horns of spinal gray matter?

       Motor output is sent through which horns of spinal gray matter?

       ii.   In which region(s) of the spinal cord will you find the lateral horns?

       iii.   Do the spinal columns contain fiber tracts or neuronal cell bodies?

II. PERIPHERAL NERVOUS SYSTEM (PNS)

A.   Cranial nerves – fill in the available table to assist you in learning the following:

   1.   Know the division and landmark of the brain from which each cranial nerve exits.
   2.   Be able to identify the twelve cranial nerves on the human brain, charts and models.
   3.   Given a diagram similar to figures found in your text, be able to state which nerve is depicted.
   4.   You must know through which foramina the nerve exits &/or enters the skull.
   5.   Know their function.

There are many useful mnemonics that can help you remember the cranial nerves. Use the one below, or make up one of your own.

Function (**S**=sensory,**M**=motor, **B**=both)

Oh - olfactory (I)	**S**ome (I)
Oh - optic (II)	**S**ay (II)
Oh - oculomotor (III)	**M**arry (III)
To - trochlear (IV)	**M**oney (IV)
Touch - trigeminal (V)	**B**ut (V)
And - abducens (VI)	**M**y (VI)
Feel - facial (VII)	**B**rother (VII)
Very - vestibulocochlear (VIII)	**S**ays (VIII)
Good - glossopharyngeal (IX)	**B**e (IX)
Velvet - vagus (X)	**B**rave (X)
Aa**H**h - accessory (XI) & hypoglossal (XII)	**M**ake (XI)
	Money (XII)

Use the space below to draw the cranial nerves on the brain &/or to make notes that will help you locate the nerves:

To assist your study of the cranial nerves please fill in the following table:

Cranial Nerve	Foramina	Origin and Course	Function
Olfactory (I)	cribriform plate	olfactory epithelium → olfactory bulb	
Optic (II)		retina → partial crossover in optic chiasma → thalamus → occipital cortex	sensory : vison
Oculomotor (III)		ventral midbrain → eye	
Trochlear (IV)		dorsal midbrain → eye	
Trigeminal (V) Ophthalmic Maxillary Mandibular		face → pons face → pons face ←→ pons	
Abducens (VI)		inferior pons → eye	

Facial (VII)		pons ←→ facial muscles and tongue	
Vestibulo-cochlear (VIII)		cochlea and vestibule → pons	
Glosso-pharyngeal (IX)		medulla oblongata ←→ throat	
Vagus (X)	jugular foramen	medulla oblongata ←→ thorax and abdomen	
Accessory (XI)		C1 – C5 spinal roots → brain stem → muscles of neck and back	motor : swallowing, neck and back muscles
Hypoglossal (XII)		medulla oblongata → tongue	

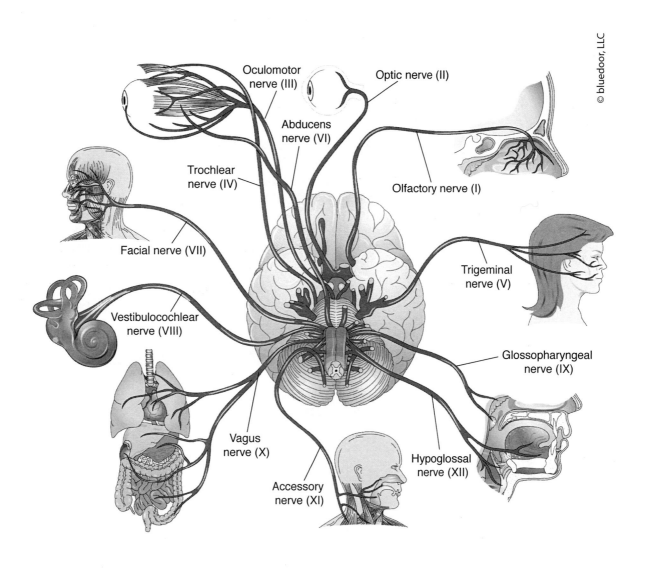

Oculomotor nerve (III)

Optic nerve (II)

Abducens nerve (VI)

Trochlear nerve (IV)

Olfactory nerve (I)

Facial nerve (VII)

Trigeminal nerve (V)

Vestibulocochlear nerve (VIII)

Glossopharyngeal nerve (IX)

Vagus nerve (X)

Accessory nerve (XI)

Hypoglossal nerve (XII)

Figure 7-3. Cranial nerves

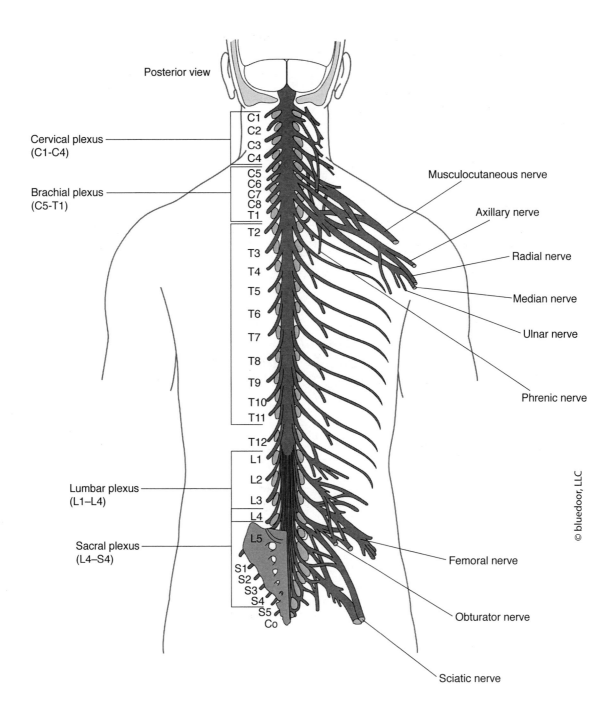

Posterior view

Cervical plexus
(C1-C4)

Brachial plexus
(C5-T1)

C1
C2
C3
C4
C5
C6
C7
C8
T1
T2
T3
T4
T5
T6
T7
T8
T9
T10
T11
T12
L1
L2
L3
L4
L5
S1
S2
S3
S4
S5
Co

Musculocutaneous nerve

Axillary nerve

Radial nerve

Median nerve

Ulnar nerve

Phrenic nerve

Lumbar plexus
(L1–L4)

Sacral plexus
(L4–S4)

Femoral nerve

Obturator nerve

Sciatic nerve

© bluedoor, LLC

Figure 7-4. Spinal nerves and their associated plexuses

B. Spinal nerves – there are thirty-one pairs of spinal nerves. Each spinal nerve is named in accordance to the level and region of the spinal cord from which it emerges. These nerves convey information between the CNS and the body via receptors, muscles, and glands. Be able to identify the following parts of a spinal nerve on the models & charts available:

dorsal root
dorsal root ganglion
ventral root
spinal nerve
dorsal ramus
ventral ramus

Draw and label a section of the spinal cord, and include in your drawing the cell body and axon of both a unipolar sensory nerve and a multipolar somatic motor nerve.

C. Nerve plexuses – The ventral rami of spinal nerves (except for $T_2 - T_{12}$) unite and mix to form a structure called a nerve plexus. From these plexuses emerge terminal nerves which innervate skin and muscles. There are four nerve plexuses. From cranial to caudal, they are the cervical, brachial, lumbar, and sacral. For all four plexuses you need to know which spinal nerves contribute to the plexuses (e.g., the brachial plexus is formed by the ventral rami of spinal nerves $C_5 - T_1$) and the major structures innervated by the nerves in each plexus.
1. cervical plexus –
  a. terminal branch
     phrenic nerve

  b. Spinal nerves= _____

  c. What structure(s) does it have motor and/or sensory control over?

2. brachial plexus – on the cadaver know the formation. Specifically be able to identify:
  a. Ventral rami
     C5
     C6
     C7
     C8
     T1
  b. trunks
     upper
     middle
     lower
  c. divisions
     anterior
     posterior
  d. cords
     lateral

        medial
        posterior
    e. terminal branches (peripheral nerves)
        (posterior cord) –
            axillary nerve
            radial nerve
        (lateral cord)-
            musculocutaneous nerve
            contribution to the median nerve
        (medial cord) –
            ulnar nerve
            contribution to the median nerve

Note: The 5 nerves listed above are the main nerves of the upper limb. However, it is important to note that the brachial plexus also gives rise to 6 other important nerves of the upper limb and trunk: the dorsal scapular nerve, the long thoracic nerve, the subscapular nerve, the thoracodorsal nerve, the suprascapular nerve and medial and lateral branches of the pectoral nerve.

    f. Spinal nerves=_____

    g. What structure(s) does it have sensory and/or motor control over?

Label the trunks, divisions, cords, and terminal branches on the following diagram. Then, use this as an example to draw your own.

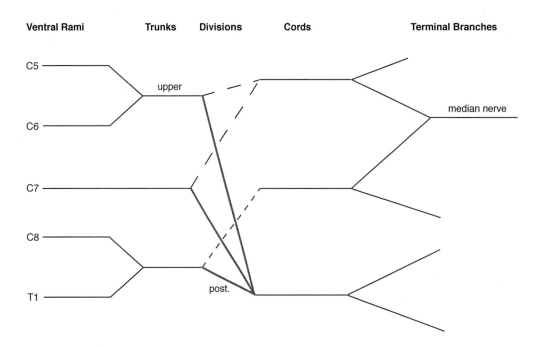

DRAW IT: The absolute best way to learn the brachial plexus is to draw and label it over and over and over and over and over...

3. lumbar plexus –
   a. terminal branches –
       femoral nerve
       obturator nerve
       ilioinguinal nerve
       lateral femoral cutaneous nerve

   b. Spinal nerves=_____

   c. What structure(s) does it have sensory and/or motor control over?

4. sacral plexus –
   a. terminal branches –
       sciatic nerve (which is really the tibial and common fibular nerves bundled together
       in a connective tissue sheath and not a separate nerve unto itsefl)
           common peroneal (fibular) nerve
           tibial nerve

   b. Spinal nerves=_____

   c. What structure(s) does it have sensory and/or motor control over?

D. Peripheral nerves – The axons of sensory and motor neurons are bundled together by
   connective tissue as they traverse between the CNS and their motor endings/sensory
   receptors. These bundles are organized muck like muscle cells in a muscle (a good time
   to review this!). Be able to identify these structures of a peripheral nerve on a figure or
   model.
   1. endoneurium
   2. perineurium
   3. fascicle
   4. epineurium
   5. associated blood vessels

SKELETAL MUSCLE INNERVATIONS

The following lists are of skeletal muscles in the upper and lower limbs and the nerves that innervate those muscles. Note: these lists are not complete, but you will only be responsible for the material in these lists for your exam. * Denotes muscles that are innervated by branches from the tibial and common fibular nerves before they split from the sciatic sheath

Musculocutaneous Nerve
Coracobrachialis
Biceps brachii
Brachialis

Median Nerve
Pronator teres
Flexor carpi radialis
Palmaris longus
Flexor digitorum superficialis
Flexor digitorum profundus
Flexor pollicis longus
Pronator quadratus

Ulnar Nerve
Flexor carpi ulnaris
Flexor digitorum profundus
Dorsal Interossei
Lumbricals

Axillary Nerve
Deltoid
Teres minor

Radial Nerve
Triceps brachii
Brachioradialis
Extensor carpi radialis longus
Extensor carpi radialis brevis
Supinator
Anconeus
Extensord digitorum
Extensor digiti minimi
Extensor carpi ulnaris
Abductor pollicis longus
Extensor pollicis longus
Extensor pollicis brevis

Extensor indicis

Femoral Nerve
Iliacus
Sartorius
Pectineus
Rectus femoris
Vastus lateralis
Vastus intermedius
Vastus medialis

Obturator Nerve
Pectineus
Adductor longus
Adductor brevis
Adductor magnus
Gracilis

Tibial Nerve
* Biceps femoris long head
* Semitendinosus
* Adductor magnus
* Semimembranosus
Gastrocnemius
Soleus
Tibialis posterior
Flexor digitorum longus
Flexor hallucis longus

Common Peroneal (Fibular) Nerve
* Biceps femoris short head
Tibialis Anterior
Peroneus (fibularis) longus
Peroneus (fibularis) brevis
Peroneus (fibularis) tertius
Extensor digitorum longus
Extensor hallucis longus

III. SENSORY SYSTEMS

A. The ear

The ear is divided into three regions, the outer (external) ear, middle ear, and inner ear.

1. External ear -
   auricle (pinna)
   external auditory canal (meatus)
   tympanic membrane

2. Middle ear (tympanic cavity) is an air filled cavity lined with a mucous membrane, located within the petrous region of the temporal bone.
   - auditory ossicles -
     - malleus
     - incus
     - stapes
   - oval window
   - round window
     - auditory tube (eustachian tube or pharyngotympanic tube)

3. Inner ear (labyrinth) is located medial to the middle ear. It consists of a **bony labyrinth** which is a series of cavities within the petrous portion of the temporal bone, and a **membranous labyrinth**. *The membranous labyrinth is a series of membranous sacs and ducts contained within the bony labyrinth*. These structures are filled with **endolymph**. The space between the membranous labyrinth and the bony labyrinth is filled with **perilymph**.
   a. Know the following structures associated with the bony labyrinth -
      vestibule
      semicircular canals
      cochlea
   b. Know the following structures associated with the membranous labyrinth -
      semicircular ducts (located within the semicircular canals)
      utricle and saccule (located within the vestibule)
      cochlear duct (located within the cochlea)
   c. internal acoustic meatus -
      Which cranial nerve is located here?

B. The eye

On models, diagrams, or real eyes, be able to identify the following:

1. Structures associated with the eye socket -
   palpebra(e) (superior and inferior)
   levator palpebrae superioris
   palpebral fissure
   lacrimal gland
   lacrimal caruncle
   lacrimal punctum
   lacrimal canaliculus (superior and inferior)
   lacrimal sac
   nasolacrimal duct

2. Structures of the eye -
cornea
sclera
iris
pupil
lens
ciliary body
anterior segment (cavity) - filled with aqueous humor
    anterior chamber
    posterior chamber
aqueous humor
posterior segment (cavity) - filled with aqueous humor
vitreous humor
choroid
retina
fovea centralis
optic disc
optic nerve
macula lutea

3. Extrinsic eye muscles (extraocular muscles) - these muscles are responsible for moving the eyeball within the bony orbit. You need to be able to identify these muscles, and also to state their action and which cranial nerve innervates them. To assist your study please use your text to fill in the following table:

Muscle	Action of the Eye	Innervation
Superior rectus		
Inferior rectus		
Medial rectus		
Lateral rectus		
Superior oblique	depresses eye and turns it laterally	IV - trochlear
Inferior oblique	elevates eye and turns it laterally	III - oculomotor

NERVOUS SYSTEM STUDY QUESTIONS

1. Name the 2 layers of the dura mater.

   A. _____ (superficial layer)

   B. _____ (deep layer)

2. Draw and label a cross section of the spinal cord.

3. Name two adult brain structures that are derived from the diencephalon.

   A. _____

   B. _____

4. The mylencephalon develops into what adult brain structure? _____

5. Name 2 lobes of the cerebrum that are supplied blood by the anterior cerebral artery.

   A. _____

   B. _____

6. Name the foramen/canal that each of the following cranial nerves passes through.

   A. Olfactory (I) _____

   B. Oculomotor (III) _____

   C. Facial (VII) _____

   D. Vagus (X) _____

   E. Hypoglossal (XII) _____

7. Draw and label the brachial plexus.

8. Name 2 extrinsic eye muscles innervated by the oculomotor nerve.

    A. _____

    B. _____

9. Name 2 membranous structures located within the vestibule.

    A. _____

    B. _____

10. What type of fluid is found in the anterior segment of the eye? _____

11. TRUE or FALSE: The tympanic membrane is part of the tympanic cavity (middle ear).

12. Which extrinsic eye muscle rolls the eye down and laterally to the side? _____

13. Located on the posterior wall of the retina, the _____ is know as the visual blind spot due to a lack of rods and cones.

14. The pigmented part of the eye is the _____.

15. Fluid collected in the lacrimal caruncle passes through an opening called the lacrimal _____ prior to entering into the lacrimal canaliculus.

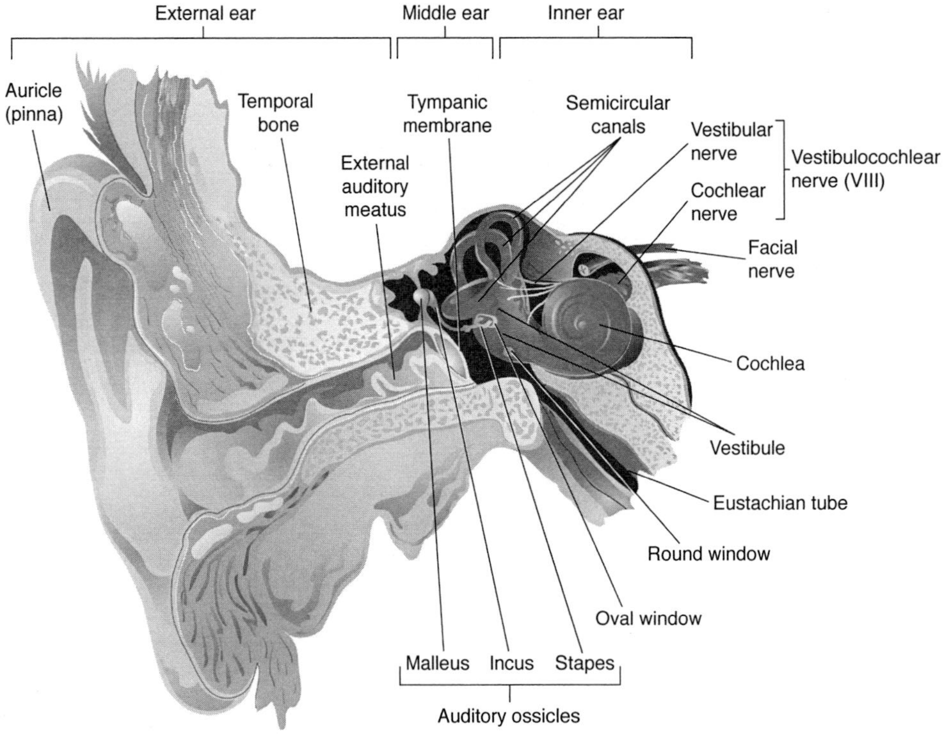

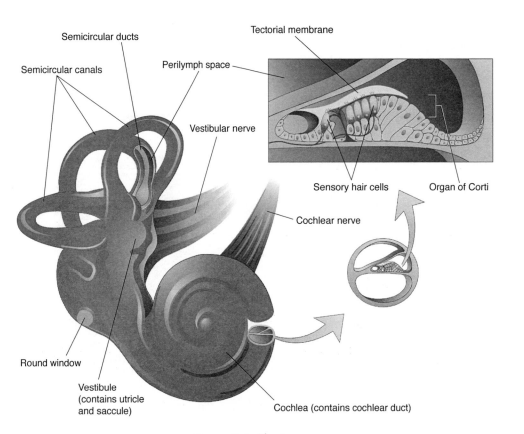

External ear   Middle ear   Inner ear

Auricle (pinna)
Temporal bone
External auditory meatus
Tympanic membrane
Semicircular canals
Vestibular nerve
Cochlear nerve
Vestibulocochlear nerve (VIII)
Facial nerve
Cochlea
Vestibule
Eustachian tube
Round window
Oval window
Malleus   Incus   Stapes
Auditory ossicles

Figure 7-5. Structures of the ear

© bluedoor, LLC

Semicircular ducts
Semicircular canals
Perilymph space
Tectorial membrane
Vestibular nerve
Sensory hair cells
Organ of Corti
Cochlear nerve
Round window
Vestibule (contains utricle and saccule)
Cochlea (contains cochlear duct)

Figure 7-6. The inner ear

© bluedoor, LLC

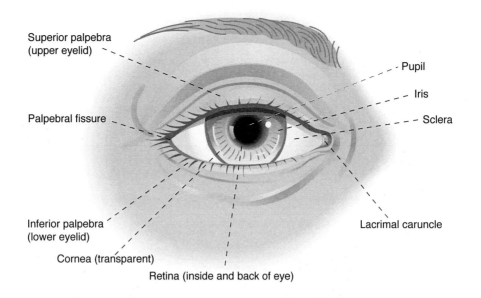

Figure 7-7. External structures of the eye

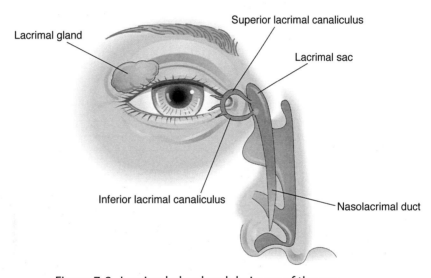

Figure 7-8. Lacrimal gland and drainage of the eye

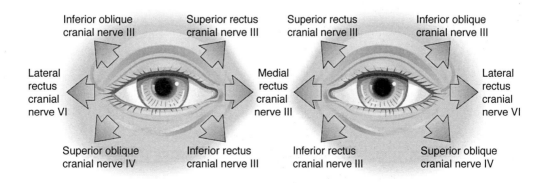

Figure 7-9. Eye movements performed by the extrinsic eye muscles

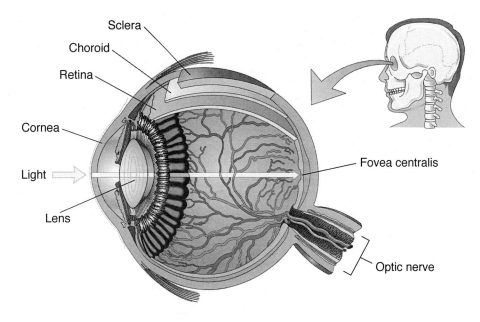

Sclera

Choroid

Retina

Cornea

Light

Lens

Fovea centralis

Optic nerve

A: Sagittal view

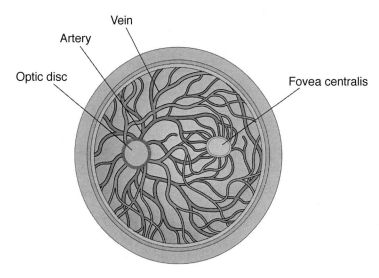

Vein

Artery

Optic disc

Fovea centralis

B: Posterior (Interior of eye)

Figure 7-10. Internal structures of the eye

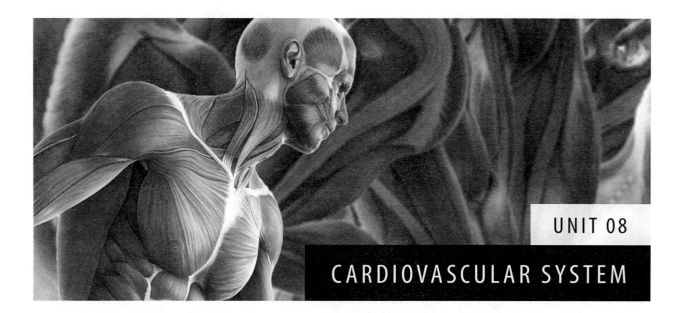

CARDIOVASCULAR SYSTEM

I. HEART

A. General considerations

    1. location - the heart is located in the thorax, just behind the sternum, in the middle mediastinum. It lies relatively free in the thorax, but is anchored at its base to the great vessels (aorta, pulmonary trunk, pulmonary veins).

    2. surfaces and borders - the heart is described as having the following surfaces and borders:

        b. **apex** - formed by the left ventricle, lies at the level of the fifth intercostal space, mid-clavicular line

        c. **base** (posterior surface) - formed by the atria, mainly the left atrium

        d. **diaphragmatic surface** (the surface that rests on the diaphragm) - formed largely by the left ventricle

        e. **sternocostal surface** (the surface that faces the sternum and costal cartilages and ribs) - formed mainly by the right ventricle and right atrium

        f. **left border** - formed by the arch of the aorta, pulmonary trunk, tip of the left auricle, and the left ventricle

        g. **right border** - formed by the superior vena cava, right atrium, inferior vena cava

    3. surface markings -

        atrioventricular groove or sulcus (coronary sulcus)

        anterior interventricular sulcus

        posterior interventricular sulcus

B. Surface projections - it is of extreme clinical importance for health care professionals to visualize the location of the normal, non-diseased heart in reference to landmarks on the anterior chest wall. Clinicians use these landmarks to 1) determine whether the heart is enlarged, and 2) to listen for heart sounds in order to assess the function of heart valves. Briefly, the heart is described as having four corners (this is for descriptive purposes only; the heart is not a square)

1. superior right corner - at the junction of the right third rib with its costal cartilage. The sounds of the aortic semilunar valve can be heard just superior to this point (at the second intercostal space)
2. inferior right corner - costal cartilage of the right sixth rib, just lateral to the sternum. The sounds of the right atrioventricular valve (tricuspid) are heard at the fifth intercostal space.
3. superior left corner - costal cartilage of the left second rib just lateral to the sternum. The sounds of the pulmonary semilunar valve are heard at the second intercostal space.
4. inferior left corner (apex)- left fifth intercostal space at the mid-clavicular line. The sounds of the left atrioventricular (mitral) valve are heard here.

LISTEN TO YOUR OWN HEART!!

It is helpful to consolidate your understanding of the position of the heart in situ by hearing the different heart sounds at different points on the thoracic wall.

C. Pericardium - the pericardium is a double layered fibrous sac which surrounds the heart and great vessels. It serves to anchor the heart in the thorax, and prevents excessive distention during activity. Be able to identify the layers of the pericardium, including the following:

1. fibrous pericardium
2. serous pericardium
    h. parietal layer - inner lining of the fibrous pericardium
    i. visceral layer - lines outer surface of heart = epicardium
    j. pericardial cavity - potential space between parietal and visceral layers of the serous pericardium.
       What is secreted here and what do you think its function is?

Draw a heart contained within the pericardium and label all the layers.

D. Heart wall – the heart wall is comprised primarily of cardiac muscle (covered in more detail at the beginning of Unit 6) supported by a connective tissue network called the **fibrous skeleton of the heart**. Be able to identify the layers of the heart wall, including:

1. Epicardium (= visceral serous pericardium)
2. Myocardium
3. Endocardium (= **endothelium**, a layer of simple squamous epithelium which is continuous throughout the entire cardiovascular system)

E. Chambers - be able to identify the following on a human heart or model:

1. right atrium and its associated structures -
   fossa ovalis
   pectinate muscles (musculi pectinati)
   right auricle
   ostium (opening) of the coronary sinus
   openings of the superior vena cava and inferior vena cava
2. interatrial septum
3. left atrium and its associated structures -
   left auricle
4. right ventricle and its associated structures -
   trabeculae carneae
   papillary muscles
   chordae tendineae
   right atrioventricular valve
   pulmonary semilunar valve
5. interventricular septum
6. left ventricle and its associated structures -
   trabeculae carneae
   papillary muscles
   chordae tendineae
   left atrioventricular valve
   aortic semilunar valve

F. Valves - The function of the two atrioventricular and two semilunar valves is similar, however the anatomy is quite different. Be sure to compare the structure of the semilunar valves to the atrioventricular valves in a human heart in which they have been exposed. Be able to identify the following on a human heart or model:

1. **right atrioventricular valve** (tricuspid) - be sure to review the structure of the valve, i.e., papillary muscles, chordae tendineae, valve cusps

2. **left atrioventricular valve** (bicuspid or mitral) - again, be sure to review the structure of the valve

3 & 4. aortic and pulmonary semilunar valves - notice how the anatomy of these two valves is very different than the atrioventricular valves. They consist of three valvules located on the inside wall of the vessel, with an arrangement reminiscent of pockets on a tee shirt.

After looking at the construction of the different valves, explain the importance of each valve as it relates to function and blood flow in the heart.

G. Great vessels - be able to identify the following on a human heart or model:
   1. systemic pump - vessels associated with the systemic circulation:
        ascending aorta
        aortic arch
        brachiocephalic artery
        left common carotid artery
        left subclavian artery
        superior vena cava
        inferior vena cava
        ligamentum arteriosum (remnant of fetal ductus arteriosus)

   2. pulmonary pump - vessels associated with the pulmonary circulation:
        pulmonary trunk
        pulmonary arteries
        pulmonary veins

H. Blood supply -
   1. coronary arteries - the right and left coronary arteries arise from the ascending aorta, just above the left ventricle while the aorta is still located posterior to the pulmonary trunk. The coronary arteries supply blood to the myocardium.
      a. left coronary artery and its branches - arises from the left side of the aorta, and as it passes behind the pulmonary trunk, bifurcates into two main branches:
         1. anterior interventricular artery (located in the anterior interventricular sulcus)
         2. circumflex artery
      a. right coronary and its branches - arises from the right side of aorta and runs in the atrioventricular groove (coronary sulcus):
         1. posterior interventricular artery
         2. marginal artery
   2. cardiac veins - the four cardiac veins drain into the **coronary sinus**.
      great cardiac vein
      middle cardiac vein
      small cardiac vein
      posterior vein of the left ventricle
  Into what does the coronary sinus drain?

II. MICROSCOPIC ANATOMY OF ARTERIES AND VEINS

There are 3 layers in the wall of both arteries and veins. These layers vary in composition and thickness based on the type of vessel and how far away they are from the heart. In general, because the blood in arteries is under higher pressure than veins, the layers in arteries are thicker with more elastin. Know the layers and structures listed below in arteries and veins, and be able to identify them on models and figures.

A. Arteries – are under high pressure, thus have thicker walls with more elastin

  1. lumen – the blood-filled space within the vessel

  2. tunica intima
     a. endothelium (simple squamous epithelium that lines the lumen)
     b. subendothelial layer – only in vessels larger than about 1 mm diameter
     c. internal elastic membrane – presence and thickness depends on vessel diameter

  3. tunica media – thickness varies by vessel diameter. Smooth muscle is innervated by the SNS and regulates vessel diameter to regulate blood flow and pressure. This is the thickest layer in muscular arteries.
     a. circular smooth muscle sheets
     b. circular sheets of elastin and collagen
     c. external elastic membrane – presence and thickness depends on vessel diameter

  4. tunica externa (also called tunica adventitia) – connective tissue with collagen and elastin that anchors the vessel to surrounding structures.
     a. vasa vasorum – arteries, capillaries, and veins in the tunica externa that supply the cells comprising the vessel wall.

B. Veins – are under lower pressure, so have thinner walls. Additionally, to ensure blood flow proceeds towards the heart, many veins have "one way" valves to prevent blood from back-flowing.

  1. lumen – as above for arteries

  2. tunica intima – less elastin than in arteries
     a. endothelium as for arteries
     b. subendothelial layer

  3. tunica media – thinner with less smooth muscle than arteries; thinner than the tunica externa of veins.
     a. circular smooth muscle
     b. circular elastin and collagen fibers

  4. tunica externa – thicker than tunica media of veins. In the venae cavae it contains longitudinal smooth muscle bands.
     a. vasa vasorum

C. Capillaries – there are 3 types of capillaries. All are formed primarily of endothelium (simple squamous epithelium) backed by varying thicknesses of basement membrane. Know examples of where each type of capillary would be found and how they differ.

1. Continuous capillaries
2. Sinusoidal capillaries
3. Fenestrated capillaries

DRAW a typical artery and a typical vein below, labeling all the different layers:

III. ARTERIAL SYSTEM

Be able to identify the following arteries and their branches. You should also know, in general terms, which structures or organs the arteries supply (in that regard, please fill in the table which appears at the end of this section). Your text has a nice outline of both arteries and veins. Also, keep in mind that some arteries are paired (i.e., left and right), while some are unpaired.

**Note: You will be required to distinguish between arteries and veins on a practical. Look carefully at where each vessel branches off and/or joins.

A. Arteries of the head and neck

1. ascending aorta (unpaired) - begins at the left ventricle and ascends to the level of the sternal angle
   a. branches -
      right coronary artery
      left coronary artery

2. arch of the aorta (unpaired) – begins at the sternal angle and runs back and to the left of the trachea and esophagus, and arches above the left main bronchus
   a. branches –
      brachiocephalic trunk (unpaired) –
         right subclavian

right vertebral artery
right internal thoracic artery
anterior intercostal arteries
right thyrocervical trunk
right costocervical trunk
right common carotid artery
right internal carotid artery
right external carotid artery
left common carotid artery –
left internal carotid artery
left external carotid artery
left subclavian artery –
left vertebral artery
left internal thoracic artery
anterior intercostal arteries
left thyrocervical trunk
left costocervical trunk

*** understand that the <u>right</u> subclavian artery gives off the same branches as the left, but that the right subclavian arises from the brachiocephalic trunk
*** understand that the <u>right</u> common carotid artery also divides into external and internal carotid arteries

3. axillary artery (paired) - as the subclavian artery passes the clavicle and 1st rib, it becomes the axillary artery. In the axilla (armpit) it gives off the following branches:
   a. branches -
      thoracoacromial trunk
      lateral thoracic artery
      subscapular artery
      posterior humeral circumflex
      anterior humeral circumflex

B. Arteries of the upper limb (paired) - as the axillary artery passes the lower border of the teres major it continues into the arm (brachium) as the brachial artery.

1. brachial artery
   a. branches -
      deep brachial artery (deep artery of arm)

2. radial artery and ulnar artery - in the cubital fossa, the brachial artery divides into its terminal branches: the radial and ulnar arteries
   a. branches - (both the radial and ulnar arteries contribute to the palmar arches)
      superficial palmar arch
      deep palmar arch

C. Arteries of the thorax

1. thoracic (descending) aorta (unpaired) - at the level of the fifth thoracic vertebra, the arch of the aorta continues in the thorax as the thoracic aorta, running from T_5 to T_{12}. The thoracic or descending aorta can be found initially to the left of the thoracic vertebral bodies, then eventually comes to lie in the midline. As the thoracic aorta passes through the aortic hiatus of the diaphragm (at the level of T_{12}) it continues into the abdomen as the abdominal aorta.

a. branches - posterior intercostal arteries (nine pairs of intercostal arteries run in the intercostal spaces)

2. internal thoracic artery (paired) - recall that the internal thoracic artery is a branch off the subclavian. It descends internally on the costal cartilages, just lateral to the sternum.

D. Arteries of the abdomen

1. abdominal aorta (unpaired) - at the level of T_{12}, as the thoracic aorta passes through the aortic hiatus of the diaphragm, it enters the abdominal cavity and continues as the abdominal aorta. The abdominal aorta can be found in the midline overlying the vertebral bodies, to the left of the inferior vena cava. At the level of L_4 the abdominal aorta bifurcates into the right and left common iliac arteries.

2. unpaired branches of the abdominal aorta -
   a. celiac trunk - the celiac trunk (artery) arises from the abdominal aorta at T_{12}. The trunk is very short and divides into three main branches. The branches of the celiac trunk supply the structures derived from the embryonic foregut (i.e. from lower third of the esophagus to the second part of the duodenum).
      i. left gastric artery
      ii. common hepatic artery – splits into gastroduodenal & hepatic artery proper

      gastroduodenal artery

      right gastroepiploic artery

      hepatic artery proper

      right gastric artery (also can branch off gastroduodenal artery)

      right hepatic artery

      left hepatic artery
      iii. splenic artery

      left gastroepiploic artery
   b. superior mesenteric artery - the branches of the superior mesenteric artery supply structures derived from the midgut (i.e. from the second part of duodenum to distal one third of the transverse colon).

      middle colic artery

      right colic artery

      ileocolic artery
   c. inferior mesenteric artery - the branches of the inferior mesenteric artery supply structures derived from the hindgut (i.e. from the distal two thirds of the transverse colon to the proximal half of the anal canal).

      sigmoid(al) artery

      left colic artery

      superior rectal artery

3. paired branches of the abdominal aorta -

   suprarenal arteries

   renal arteries

   gonadal arteries

E. Arteries of the pelvis - at the level of L$_4$ the abdominal aorta divides into the right and left common iliac arteries. At the pelvic inlet in front of the sacroiliac joint, each common iliac artery bifurcates into an external and internal iliac artery.

   1. internal iliac artery (paired) - the internal iliac artery divides into an anterior and posterior division. The branches of the internal iliac artery supply the muscular walls and viscera of the pelvis, structures associated with the perineum, and external genitalia. The branching patterns of the internal iliac artery are highly variable and can be difficult to see on some cadavers. You will be required to identify the branches of the internal iliac artery if visible and you will be required to know the structures to which they supply blood.

Branches of the Internal Iliac Artery	Supplies Blood to:
Gluteal arteries	gluteal muscles
superior gluteal artery	
inferior gluteal artery	
Obturator artery	thigh adductor muscles
Internal pudendal artery	perineum (anus, vulva or posterior scrotum)

   2. external iliac artery (paired) - as the external iliac artery passes under the inguinal ligament it continues into the lower limb as the femoral artery.

    F. Arteries of the lower limb - (paired)

   1. femoral artery - the femoral artery and its branches and terminal divisions supply all the structures of the lower limb. To locate the femoral artery, look for a region known as the **femoral triangle**. The femoral triangle is an area located on the medial aspect of the thigh. Its superior border is the inguinal ligament, lateral border is the sartorius, and the medial border is the adductor longus. The femoral triangle is an important area because it contains (from lateral to medial) the femoral nerve, femoral artery, femoral vein, and lymphatics (inguinal lymph nodes). A good mnemonic for remembering the order (lateral to medial) in which you will find the structures in the femoral triangle is NAVeL (nerve, artery, vein, lymphatics).

   a. branches -
   deep femoral artery (deep artery of thigh)

   2. popliteal artery - as the femoral artery descends toward the knee, it passes from the medial compartment to the posterior compartment of the thigh by passing through the adductor canal. The adductor canal is a passageway through the adductor magnus muscle. As the femoral artery emerges from the canal in the posterior aspect of the thigh it enters the popliteal fossa and continues inferiorly as the popliteal artery.

3. anterior tibial artery - in the popliteal fossa the popliteal artery divides into two terminal branches, the anterior tibial artery and the posterior tibial artery. The anterior tibial artery gains entrance to the anterior compartment of the leg by passing through an opening in the interosseous membrane. It then courses inferiorly on the anterior surface of the interosseous membrane. As the anterior tibial artery passes under the extensor retinaculum it continues into the foot as the dorsalis pedis artery.

a. branches -
   dorsalis pedis artery - the pulsation of the dorsalis pedis artery can be felt on the dorsum of the foot. It can be felt between the tendon of the extensor hallucis longus (medial side) and the extensor digitorum (lateral side)

4. posterior tibial artery - one of the terminal branches of the popliteal artery, the posterior tibial artery can be found on the posterior aspect of the tibia.

a. branches -
   peroneal artery - the peroneal artery arises close to the origin of the posterior tibial artery and can be found in close association with the fibula, or running within the substance of the flexor hallucis longus muscle

Artery	Branch of?	Supplies Blood to:
Right coronary	aorta	
Left coronary	aorta	
External carotid	common carotid	
Internal carotid	common carotid	
Vertebral	subclavian	
Internal thoracic (mammary)	subclavian	
Thyrocervical trunk	subclavian	
Costocervical trunk	subclavian	deep muscles of the neck and the two superior intercostal spaces
Thoracoacromial trunk	axillary	pectoralis and deltoid muscles
Posterior humeral circumflex	axillary	deltoid muscle and shoulder joint
Anterior humeral circumflex	axillary	deltoid muscle and shoulder joint
Brachial	axillary	
Deep brachial	brachial	triceps brachii
Radial	brachial	
Ulnar	brachial	
Superficial palmar arches	radial and ulnar	
Deep palmar arches	radial and ulnar	
Posterior intercostal	descending aorta	
Left gastric	celiac trunk	
Right gastric	common hepatic	lesser curvature of stomach
Gastroduodenal	common hepatic	pancreas and duodenum
Right hepatic	hepatic artery proper	liver
Left hepatic	hepatic artery proper	liver
Splenic	celiac trunk	

Artery	Branch of?	Supplies Blood to:
Superior mesenteric	abdominal aorta	
Inferior mesenteric	abdominal aorta	
Renal	abdominal aorta	
Gonadal	abdominal aorta	
Suprarenal	Renal	Adrenal gland
Femoral	external iliac	
Deep femoral	femoral	
Anterior tibial	popliteal	
Dorsalis pedis	anterior tibial	
Posterior tibial	popliteal	
Peroneal	posterior tibial	

Digestive Blood Supply: Fill in the main artery (or arteries) that supply blood to the following organs:

Organ	Arterial Supply By
Stomach	Left and right gastric, gastroduodenal
Duodenum	
Jejunum	
Large intestine	
Liver	
Gallbladder	
Pancreas	
Spleen	

DRAW IT: One of the best ways to visualize and learn the most common arterial branching patterns is to draw and label it over and over and over ...

DRAW IT: One of the best ways to visualize and learn the most common venous merging patterns is to draw and label it over and over and over ...

ONE MORE TIME: Below are all the arteries listed previously, but to help you in reviewing the vessels all extraneous text has been removed. This may not be a complete list, so please be sure to read carefully through the previous material.

A. Arteries of the head and neck
1. ascending aorta-
   a. branches -
      right coronary artery -
         posterior interventricular artery
         marginal artery
      left coronary artery
         anterior interventricular artery
         circumflex artery
2. arch of the aorta -
   a. branches -
      brachiocephalic trunk -
         right subclavian
         right common carotid arteries
      left & right common carotid artery -
         external carotid artery
         internal carotid artery
      left & right subclavian artery -
         vertebral artery
         internal thoracic artery
            anterior intercostal arteries
         thyrocervical trunk
         costocervical trunk
3. axillary artery -
   a. branches -
      thoracoacromial trunk
      lateral thoracic artery
      subscapular artery
      posterior humeral circumflex
      anterior humeral circumflex

B. Arteries of the upper limb
1. brachial artery
   a. branches -
      deep brachial artery
2. radial artery and ulnar artery -
   a. branches -
      superficial palmar arch
      deep palmar arch

C. Arteries of the thorax
1. thoracic (descending) aorta -
   a. branches -
      posterior intercostal arteries

D. Arteries of the abdomen
  1. abdominal aorta -
  2. unpaired branches of the abdominal aorta -
     a. celiac trunk -
        i. left gastric artery
        ii. common hepatic artery -
              gastroduodenal artery
                 right gastroepiploic artery
              hepatic artery proper
                 right hepatic artery
                 left hepatic artery
                 right gastric artery
        iii. splenic artery
              left gastroepiploic artery
     b. superior mesenteric artery -
           middle colic artery
           right colic artery
           ileocolic artery
     c. inferior mesenteric artery -
           sigmoidal artery
           left colic artery
           superior rectal artery
  3. paired branches of the abdominal aorta -
        suprarenal arteries
        renal arteries
        gonadal arteries

E. Arteries of the pelvis –
  1. common iliac artery
     a. internal iliac artery
        superior gluteal artery
        inferior gluteal artery
        obturator artery
        internal pudendal artery
     b. external iliac artery

F. Arteries of the lower limb
  1. femoral artery -
     a. deep femoral artery (profunda femoris a.)
  2. popliteal artery -
  3. anterior tibial artery -
     a. dorsalis pedis artery
  4. posterior tibial artery -
     a. peroneal artery

IV. VENOUS SYSTEM

In general, veins parallel arteries, and oftentimes take the same name as the artery with which they run. For some moderate sized arteries (e.g., brachial, radial), there may be two veins accompanying the artery. However, there is a system of more superficial veins which do not conform to this pattern. These veins run in the subcutaneous tissue, and more often than not, can be seen through the skin. For example, the vein from which blood is generally drawn (located in the cubital fossa) is the median cubital vein. Note, there are no accompanying arteries with the superficial veins. Why do you think this is so?

It is important to remember that all blood sent to the periphery of the body must be returned to the heart, specifically to the right atrium, through a series of vessels called veins (the venous system). The peripheral veins can be classified as those that drain into the superior vena cava and those that drain into the inferior vena cava.

A. Veins draining to the Superior Vena Cava – as a general rule, all veins superior to the diaphragm are drained by the superior vena cava. The superior vena cava is formed by the union of the **left** and **right brachiocephalic** veins.

Be able to identify the following veins on the cadavers and models. Sometimes superficial veins are cut away during dissections – your TA will inform you if any superficial veins are not visible on the cadavers.

1. Veins of the head, neck, and upper limb
    cephalic vein
    basilic vein
    median cubital vein
    subclavian vein
    external jugular vein
    internal jugular vein
    right/left brachiocephalic veins
    superior vena cava
2. Veins of the thoracic cavity
    hemiazygos vein
    posterior intercostal vein
    accessory hemiazygos vein
    azygos vein
    superior vena cava

B. Veins draining to the Inferior Vena Cava – as a general rule all veins inferior to the diaphragm are drained by the inferior vena cava. The inferior vena cava is formed by the union of the left and right common iliac veins.
1. veins of the lower limbs
    great saphenous vein
    femoral vein

2. Veins of the abdominal and pelvic cavity
    external iliac vein
    internal iliac vein

left/right common iliac vein
inferior vena cava
gonadal vein
renal vein
 suprarenal vein

C. Hepatic portal system -
The portal system drains the gastrointestinal tract from the stomach to the rectum, and delivers this blood to the liver sinusoids.

What is the significance (physiological importance) of this arrangement?

The **hepatic portal vein** is formed posterior to the pancreas by the union of the splenic and superior mesenteric veins. Be able to identify the following tributaries of the hepatic portal system:
hepatic portal vein
splenic vein
superior mesenteric vein
inferior mesenteric vein

CARDIOVASCULAR SYSTEM STUDY QUESTIONS

1. The _____ valve is found between the right ventricle and the pulmonary trunk.

2. The _____ valve is found between the left atrium from the left ventricle.

3. Name an artery that supplies blood to the following structures.

    Jejunum _____

    Flexor hallucis longus _____

    Triceps brachii _____

    Brain and spinal cord _____

    Lesser curvature of the stomach _____

    Pericardium _____

4. TRUE or FALSE: The tunica media is thicker in the walls of an artery than in the walls of a vein.

5. Which 2 veins join to form the superior vena cava?

    A. _____

    B. _____

6. Which muscle forms the medial border of the femoral triangle? _____

    Which artery supplies blood to this muscle? _____

7. Name the 3 vessels that drain into the right atrium.

    A. _____

    B. _____

    C. _____

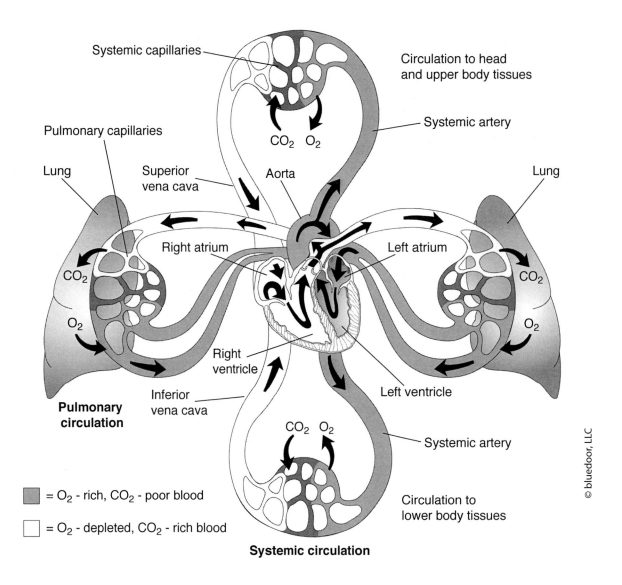

Systemic capillaries

Circulation to head
and upper body tissues

Systemic artery

Pulmonary capillaries

Lung

Superior
vena cava

Aorta

Lung

CO_2 O_2

Right atrium

Left atrium

CO_2

CO_2

O_2

O_2

Right
ventricle

Inferior
vena cava

Left ventricle

**Pulmonary
circulation**

CO_2 O_2

Systemic artery

= O_2 - rich, CO_2 - poor blood

= O_2 - depleted, CO_2 - rich blood

Circulation to
lower body tissues

Systemic circulation

Figure 8-1. Systemic and pulmonary circulation

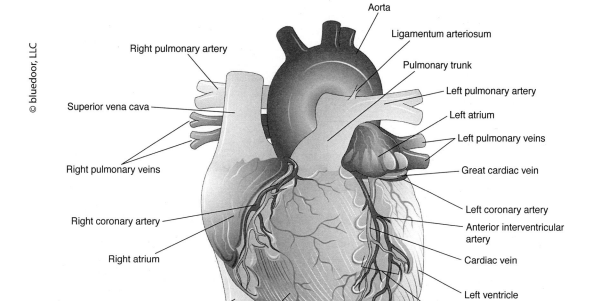

Figure 8-2. Anterior view of heart

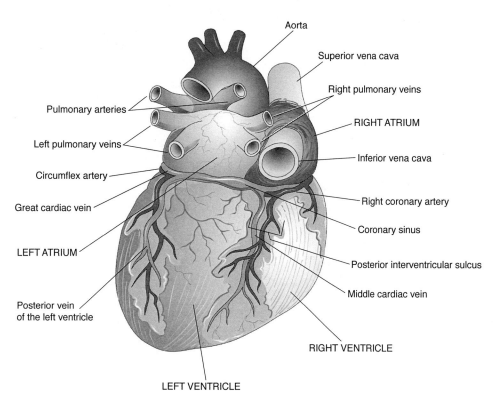

Figure 8-3. Posterior view of heart

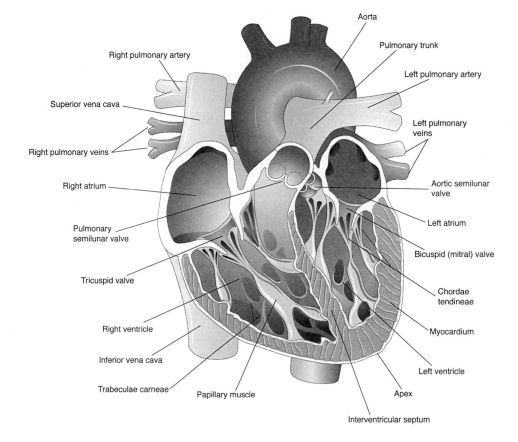

Figure 8-4. Anterior view of internal structures of the heart

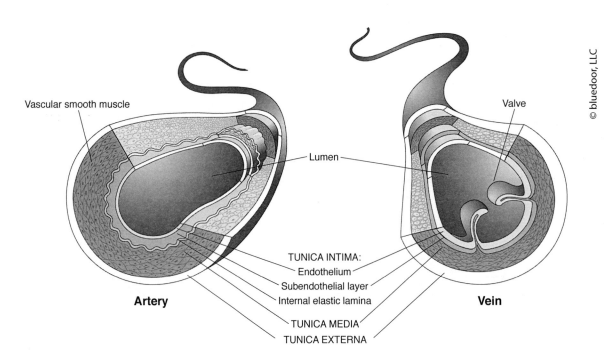

Figure 8-5. Comparison of an artery and vein

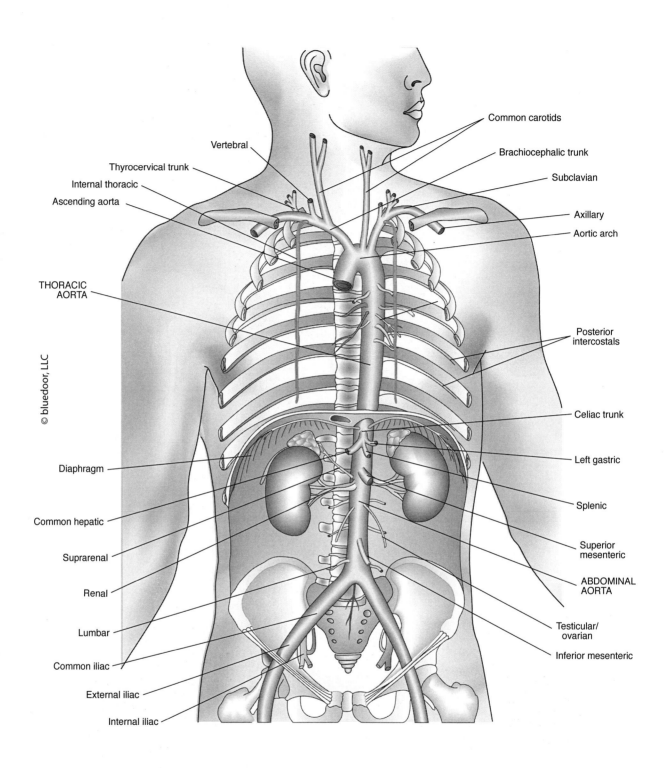

Figure 8-6 (a). Larger arteries of the body

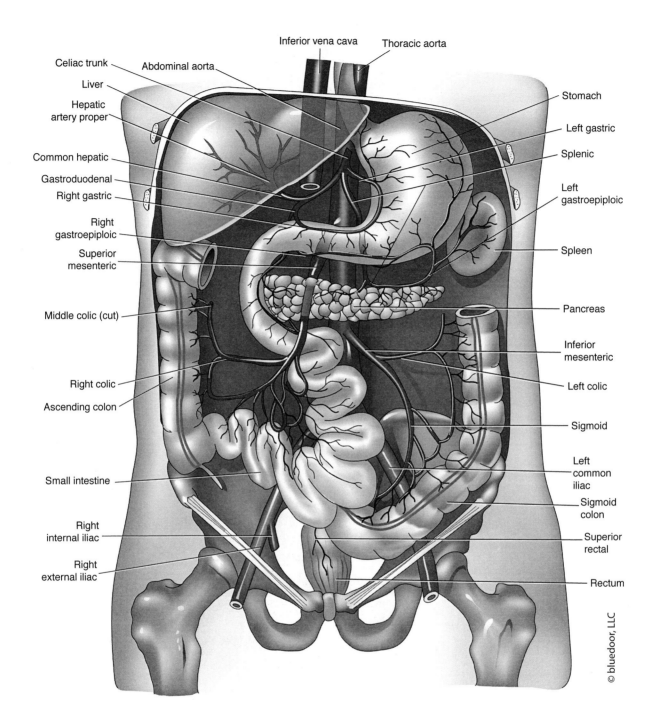

Inferior vena cava

Thoracic aorta

Celiac trunk

Abdominal aorta

Liver

Hepatic artery proper

Common hepatic

Gastroduodenal

Right gastric

Right gastroepiploic

Superior mesenteric

Middle colic (cut)

Right colic

Ascending colon

Small intestine

Right internal iliac

Right external iliac

Stomach

Left gastric

Splenic

Left gastroepiploic

Spleen

Pancreas

Inferior mesenteric

Left colic

Sigmoid

Left common iliac

Sigmoid colon

Superior rectal

Rectum

© bluedoor, LLC

Figure 8-6 (b). Larger arteries of the abdominopelvic cavity.

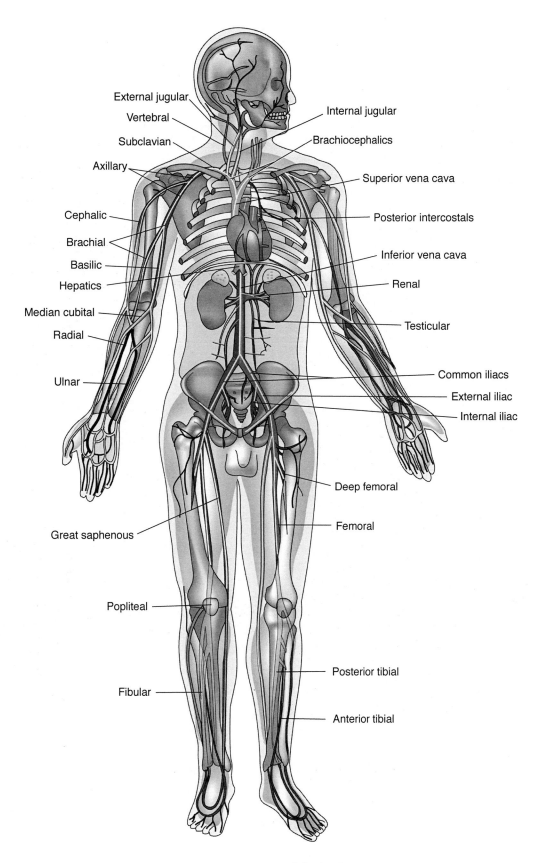

External jugular
Vertebral
Subclavian
Axillary
Cephalic
Brachial
Basilic
Hepatics
Median cubital
Radial
Ulnar
Great saphenous
Popliteal
Fibular

Internal jugular
Brachiocephalics
Superior vena cava
Posterior intercostals
Inferior vena cava
Renal
Testicular
Common iliacs
External iliac
Internal iliac
Deep femoral
Femoral
Posterior tibial
Anterior tibial

Figure 8-7. Larger veins of the body

RESPIRATORY SYSTEM

I. GENERAL CONSIDERATIONS

A. The respiratory system is often divided into the **upper respiratory tract**, bounded by the orifices externally and the false vocal folks inferiorly, and the **lower respiratory tract**, which runs from the true vocal folks to the alveoli. The lower respiratory tract can be functionally divided into two zones.

1. The respiratory zone = site of gas exchange, consists of respiratory bronchioles and alveoli in the lung

2. The conducting zone = portions of respiratory system whose function is to conduct air to the respiratory zone.

II. ANATOMY

(Most of the structures of the upper respiratory tract are best studied on the bisected head model)

A. Nasal cavity - extends from the **external nares** (nostrils) in front, to the **choanae** (posterior nares) behind. Boundaries are:

floor = hard palate (formed by palatine process of the maxillary bone and the horizontal process of the palatine bone)

roof = contributions from the sphenoid, ethmoid, frontal, nasal bones

lateral walls = superior, middle, and inferior concha

B. Paranasal sinuses - are mucus lined, air filled cavities found in some of the bones of the skull. Each sinus drains into the nasal cavity in close relation to one of the conchae. Be able to identify the following paranasal sinuses (these should be familiar - they were identified in Unit 4) and their sites of drainage.

maxillary
frontal
sphenoid
ethmoid

Sinus	Site of Drainage
Maxillary	middle meatus
Frontal	middle meatus
Sphenoid	sphenoethmoidal recess (above superior nasal concha)
Ethmoid	superior and middle meatus

C. Pharynx - the funnel-shaped region posterior to the nasal and oral cavities and the larynx. The inferior end is continuous with the esophagus. It is divided into three regions. Know the regions and the structures of the pharynx.

1. tonsils -

   pharyngeal tonsil
   palatine tonsils
   lingual tonsil

2. uvula
3. soft palate
4. pharyngotympanic (auditory) tube

Know the following regions, their boundaries and contents. Use your textbook to help complete the table below:

Region	Boundaries	Structure(s)
Nasopharynx		
Oropharynx	from soft palate to epiglottis	palatine tonsils lingual tonsil
Laryngopharynx		NONE

D. Larynx - on the models or diagrams provided in the lab identify the following structures associated with the larynx:

1. cartilages – six cartilages makes up the framework of the larynx, three are paired, three are unpaired

   thyroid cartilage (unpaired)
       laryngeal prominence
   cricoid cartilage (unpaired)
   arytenoid cartilage (paired)
   corniculate cartilage (paired)
   cuneiform cartilage (paired)
   epiglottis (unpaired)

2. ligaments -
        vocal folds (true vocal cords)
           rima glottidis
        vestibular folds (false vocal cords)
    Note: the glottis is the rima glottidis plus the true vocal folds.

E. Trachea and tracheal cartilages -
    What is the carina?

F. Bronchial tree - know the divisions of the bronchial tree and, using your text, be able to answer the following questions.
        trachea
        primary (main) bronchus (bronchi)
        secondary (lobar) bronchus (bronchi)
        tertiary (segmental) bronchus (bronchi)

1. What are the differences between the right and left primary bronchi?

2. Think of a clinical reason why it might be important to know the differences between the right & left primary bronchi.

G. Lungs -
    1. general characteristics - except for the mediastinum (see below) the thoracic cavity is filled by the paired lungs. Both lungs are described as having the following borders and surfaces, which you should be able to identify:
        apex
        base
        costal surface
        mediastinal surface
        diaphragmatic surface

On the mediastinal surface of each lung is found the:
root of the lung =
    1. pulmonary arteries
    2. pulmonary veins
    3. bronchi

hilum = area (indentation) through which the structures at the root pass into lung stroma

    2. right lung -
        superior (upper) lobe
        middle lobe
        inferior (lower) lobe
        oblique fissure
        horizontal fissure

3. left lung -
    superior (upper) lobe
    inferior (lower) lobe
    oblique fissure
    cardiac notch
    lingula

H. Diaphragm - the principle muscle of respiration is the diaphragm. It is a dome shaped muscular and tendinous structure which separates the thoracic and abdominal cavities. Many structures pass from the thoracic cavity into the abdominal cavity. The three largest structures that pass through the diaphragm are the descending aorta, the esophagus and the inferior vena cava. The diaphragm is said to have three openings or **hiatuses** where these structures pass through (the caval hiatus, the esphageal hiatus, and the aortic hiatus).

I. Mediastinum - review the boundaries and contents of the mediastinum.

RESPIRATORY SYSTEM STUDY QUESTIONS

1. Name 2 structures found within the oropharynx.

    A. _____

    B. _____

2. The cartilage situated at the point where the trachea divides into the two primary bronchi is referred to as the _____.

3. Name 2 sinuses drained by the middle meatus.

    A. _____

    B. _____

4. Name the 3 diaphragmatic hiatuses.

    A. _____

    B. _____

    C. _____

5. The root of the lung is found on which surface of the lung?

6. What is the difference between the glottis and the rima glottidis?

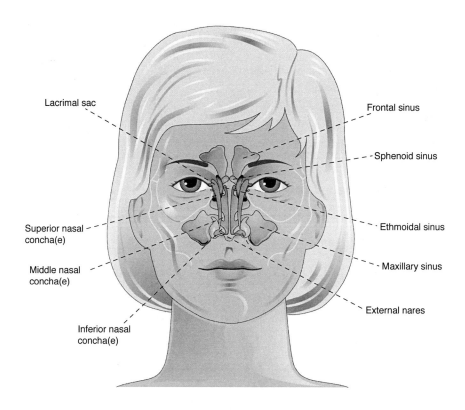

Figure 9-1. Sinuses and structures associated with the nasal cavity

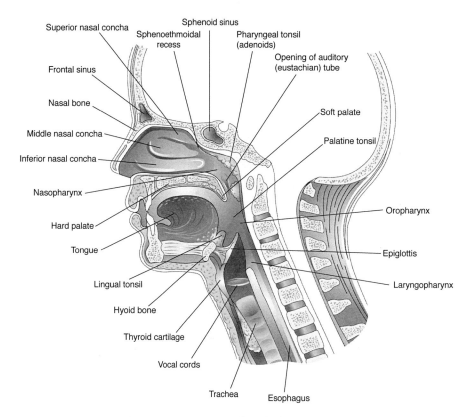

Figure 9-2. Structures associated with the respiratory system

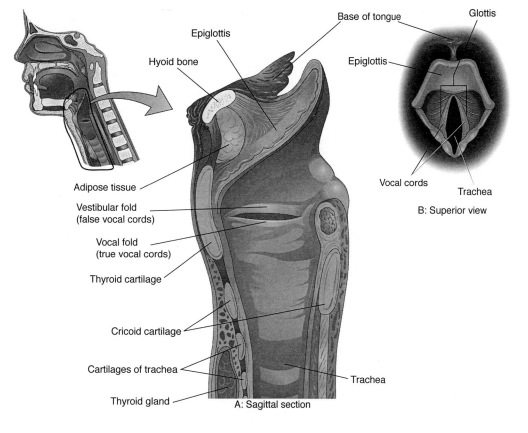

Base of tongue

Glottis

Epiglottis

Epiglottis

Hyoid bone

Vocal cords

Trachea

B: Superior view

Adipose tissue

Vestibular fold
(false vocal cords)

Vocal fold
(true vocal cords)

Thyroid cartilage

Cricoid cartilage

Cartilages of trachea

Trachea

Thyroid gland

A: Sagittal section

Figure 9-3. Lateral view of a bisected larynx

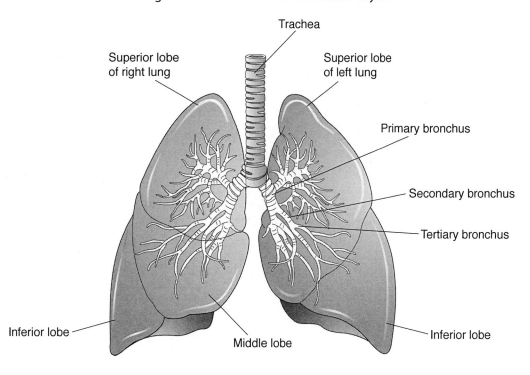

Trachea

Superior lobe
of right lung

Superior lobe
of left lung

Primary bronchus

Secondary bronchus

Tertiary bronchus

Inferior lobe

Inferior lobe

Middle lobe

Figure 9-4. Bronchial tree and lobes of the lungs

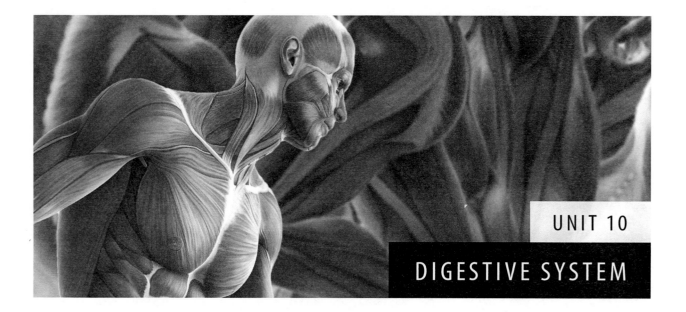

DIGESTIVE SYSTEM

I. MICROSCOPIC ANATOMY

The following objectives will be used to guide our exploration of the gastrointestinal (GI) tract:
    1) to describe the general structure of the gastrointestinal tract
    2) to be able to distinguish among different regions of the gastrointestinal tract

A. General structure

Throughout its length, the wall of the gastrointestinal tract is composed of four principal layers. **You will need to be able to identify these layers on slides, models and figures in each region of the digestive tract.** The composition of these four layers changes throughout the tract, based on function. You should be able to correlate regional differences in each layer with changing function in each region.

1. **mucosal layer** – adjacent to the lumen of the canal. It is an epithelial membrane which functions to:

   1 – secrete mucus, digestive enzymes or hormones
   2 – absorb products of digestion (small intestine) or water, electrolytes and vitamins (large intestine)

   Sublayers of the mucosa:
   epithelial lining – varies from simple columnar to stratified sauamous epithelium, depending on location and function.
   lamina propria – composed of loose areolar connective tissue
   muscularis mucosae – composed of smooth muscle

2. **submucosa** – surrounds mucosa; consists of loose connective tissue surrounding nerves, and blood and lymphatic vessels. Contains the submucosal (or Meissner's) plexus which helps regulate secretion and motility.

3. **muscularis externa** – surrounds submucosa; consists of two layers of smooth muscle, an inner circular layer, and an outer longitudinal layer. The structure of the muscularis externa is responsible for segmentation and peristaltic activity of the alimentary tract. The myenteric (or Auerbach's) nerve plexus is sandwiched between the circular and longitudinal layers, where it helps regulate contraction.

4. **serosa** – serous membrane that covers the muscularis externa. It is found along most of the digestive tract. Regions of the tract that are not within the abdominopelvic cavity are instead surrounded by adventitia. The serosa is the visceral layer of the serous membrane (also called visceral peritoneum). Remember from Unit 2 that there is also a parietal layer of serous membrane lining the abdominopelvic cavity (also called parietal peritoneum). Additionally, serous membrane also lines the pleural and pericardial cavities (closed body cavities).

B. Specific regions:

***IN EACH OF THE SPECIFIC REGIONS BE ABLE TO IDENTIFY THE FOLLOWING LAYERS:

    mucosa
        epithelium
        lamina propria
        muscularis mucosae
    submucosa
    muscularis externa
        circular layer
        longitudinal layer
        oblique layer (stomach only)
    serosa or adventitia

1. esophagus – is a muscular collapsible tube which conducts swallowed food from the pharynx above to the stomach below. Microscopic features include (but are not limited to):
   a. notice the lumenal epithelium as it differs from the rest of the alimentary tract
   b. mucous glands located in the submucosa
   c. the superior third of the muscularis externa contains skeletal muscle
   d. adventitia covers the muscularis externa layer; there is no serosal layer

Draw and label the layers and structures of the esophagus below:

2. stomach – situated in the superior portion of the abdomen, it is roughly J-shaped. Its functions include storage, some digestion, and release of food into the duodenum. Microscopic features include (but are not limited to):

a. gastric pits with mucus-secreting goblet cells, pepsinogen-secreting chief cells, HCl-secreting parietal cells, and hormone-secreting enteroendocrine cells.
b. muscularis externa which contains a circular, **oblique** and longitudinal smooth muscle layer

Draw and label the layers and structures of the stomach below:

3. small intestine – nearly all absorption of nutrients occurs in the small intestine. To increase absorptive area the small intestine displays many luminal modifications. Some of these modifications are:
   a. plicae circulares – permanent folds of mucosa and submucosa
   b. intestinal villi – finger-like projections of the mucosa (epithelium and lamina propria, only).
   c. microvilli – extensions of the apical membrane of the epithelial cells.

Other modifications support digestion of ingested foodstuffs by adding enzymes, bile, and other digestive juices, as well as producing mucus and alkaline fluid to help protect the lining of the small intestine:

   a. hepatopancreatic ampulla (ampulla of Vater) – the inlet of the united ducts of the gallbladder and pancreas through which bile, pancreatic enzymes, and alkaline pancreatic juice enter the duodenum.
   b. intestinal crypts (crypts of Lieberkuhn) – pits between the villi lined with epithelial cells which secrete intestinal juice, as well as Paneth cells which secrete enzymes that target some bacteria and help others.
   c. duodenal glands (Brunner's glands) – in the duodenum only, these compound tubular glands embedded in the submucosa release alkaline mucus into the intestinal crypts.
   d. Payer's patches (aggregated lymphoid nodules) – large mucosa-associated lymphatic tissue (MALT) patches found in the submucosa of the ileum.

Draw and label the layers and structures of the small intestine below:

4. large intestine – little or no digestion takes place in the large intestine; its function is largely water and electrolyte absorption. This is reflected in the fact that villi are not present in the large intestine. Also, the longitudinal layer of the muscularis externa is reduced to three strips, which form **teniae coli**.

Draw and label the layers and structures of the large intestine below:

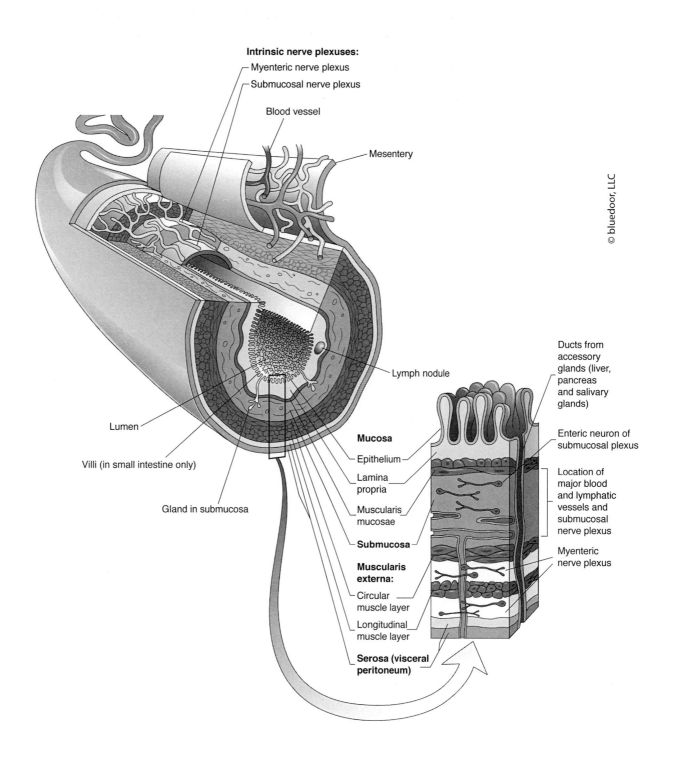

Figure 10-1. Layers of the GI tract

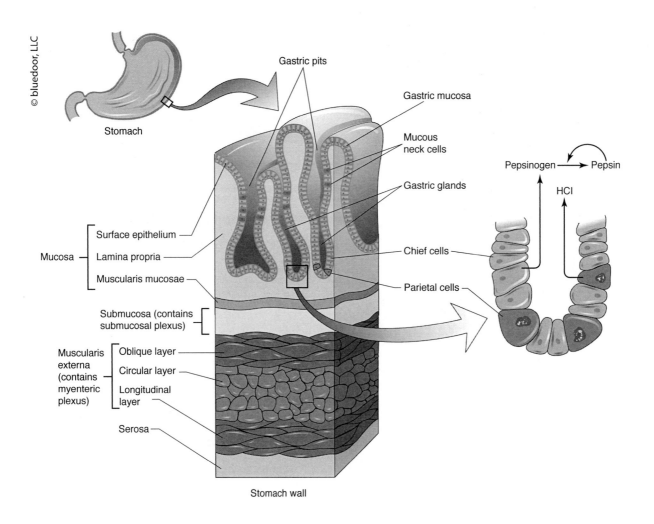

Stomach

Gastric pits

Gastric mucosa

Mucous neck cells

Gastric glands

Surface epithelium

Mucosa

Lamina propria

Muscularis mucosae

Chief cells

Parietal cells

Submucosa (contains submucosal plexus)

Muscularis externa (contains myenteric plexus)

Oblique layer

Circular layer

Longitudinal layer

Serosa

Stomach wall

Pepsinogen ⟶ Pepsin

HCl

Figure 10-2. The stomach wall

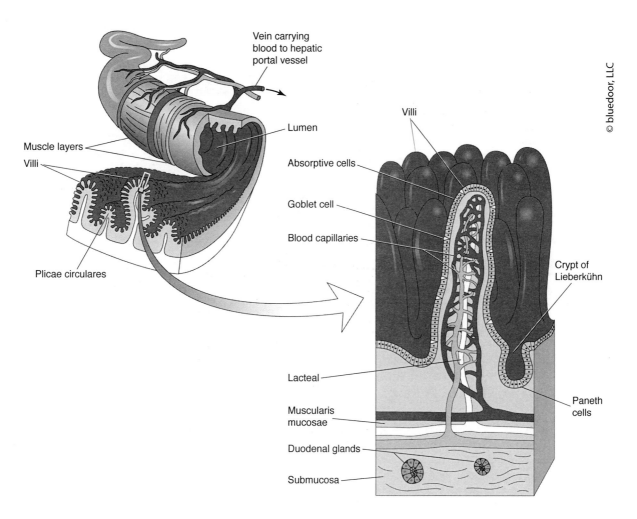

Vein carrying
blood to hepatic
portal vessel

Lumen

Muscle layers

Villi

Plicae circulares

Villi

Absorptive cells

Goblet cell

Blood capillaries

Crypt of
Lieberkühn

Lacteal

Paneth
cells

Muscularis
mucosae

Duodenal glands

Submucosa

Figure 10-3. The small intestine

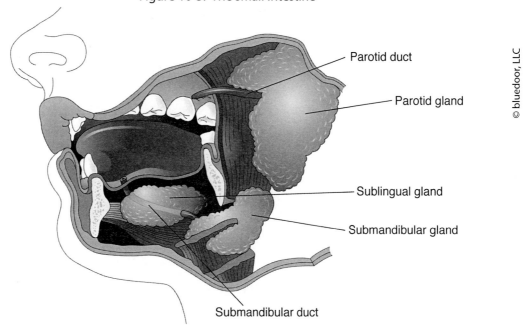

Parotid duct

Parotid gland

Sublingual gland

Submandibular gland

Submandibular duct

Figure 10-4. Salivary glands

C. Based on the previous information, and using your text as a reference, fill in the table below:

Organ	Type of Lumenal Epithelium	Specialized Cell Types or Distinguishing Features
Esophagus		
Stomach	simple columnar	gastric pits, muscularis externa
Small intestine		
Large intestine		

II. PERITONEUM AND PERITONEAL CAVITY

The peritoneum is a thin serous membrane that lines the walls and covers most organs of the abdominal and pelvic cavities. It is a double-layered membrane made up of a visceral (pertaining to organs) and a parietal (pertaining to body wall) layer. The peritoneal cavity is a potential space between the two layers of the peritoneum. Specialized regions of the peritoneum take on different names and functions.

A. Be able to identify the following named regions of the peritoneum:

> mesentery proper
> greater omentum
> lesser omentum
> falciform ligament
> ligamentum teres

B. Define the following terms as they relate to the peritoneal cavity:

> intraperitoneal-

> retroperitoneal-

Note the difference between "secondarily retroperitoneal" and "retroperitoneal". An organ, such as the kidney that did not ever enter the abdomnopelvic cavity during development is "retroperitoneal". Organs such as the duodenum and ascending colon that were in the peritoneal cavity at some point developmentally, but which later fuse with the body wall, are considered "secondarily retroperitoneal". You will need to know whether an abdominal organ is intraperitoneal or retroperitoneal. After completing the following section, place the digestive organs in the appropriate column.

Intraperitoneal   Secondarily retroperitoneal

III. GROSS ANATOMY

Be able to identify the following structures and organs on the cadaver and models available in the lab. **You must also know the blood supply to the organs of the digestive system, which was discussed in Unit 8.**

A. Oral cavity – the mouth, or oral cavity, extends from the lips anteriorly to its junction with the oropharynx posteriorly. Important contents of the oral cavity are:
   1. teeth
   2. tongue
   3. hard and soft palate
B. Salivary glands –
   1. parotid gland & parotid duct
      Where can you find the opening of the parotid duct into the oral cavity?

   2. submandibular gland (submaxillary gland)
   3. sublingual gland

C. Oropharynx (review boundaries and structures from Respiratory System)

D. Laryngopharynx (review boundaries and structures from Respiratory System)

E. Esophagus
   1. cardiac sphincter

F. Stomach -

   cardia
   fundus
   body
   greater curvature
   lesser curvature
   rugae
   pylorus
   pyloric sphincter

   What peritoneal structure is found attached to the greater curvature?

   _____

   What peritoneal structure is found attached to the lesser curvature?

   _____

G. Small intestine
   1. duodenum –
         common bile duct
   2. jejunum and ileum –
         the mesentery proper

H. Large intestine (colon) –

   ileocecal junction/valve
   cecum
   vermiform appendix
   ascending colon
   hepatic (right colic) flexure
   transverse colon
   splenic (left colic) flexure
   descending colon
   sigmoid colon
   rectum
   anus
   tenia(*e*) coli <u>or</u> taenia(*e*) coli (both spellings are acceptable)
   epiploic appendages

I. Liver and gallbladder

   1. liver
       a. surfaces –
           diaphragmatic
           visceral
       b. lobes –
           right
           left
           caudate
           quadrate
       c. ligaments –
           falciform
           ligamentum teres (round ligament)
       d. porta hepatis -
           hepatic arteries, right and left
           hepatic portal vein
           right and left hepatic ducts
           common hepatic duct - joins cystic duct to form the common bile duct

What is the porta hepatis?

   2. gallbladder –
       cystic duct
       common bile duct
J. Pancreas –
   head
   body
   tail

K. Spleen and appendix – The spleen and the appendix are part of the lymphatic system, not the digestive system; however, the lymphatic system is not covered in detail in lab, so we will look at these structures as we consider the digestive tract.

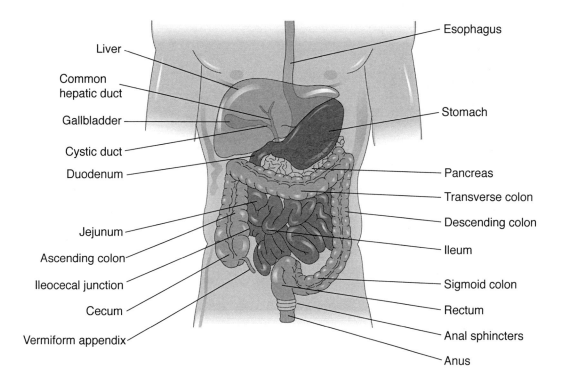

Figure 10-5. Organs of the digestive system

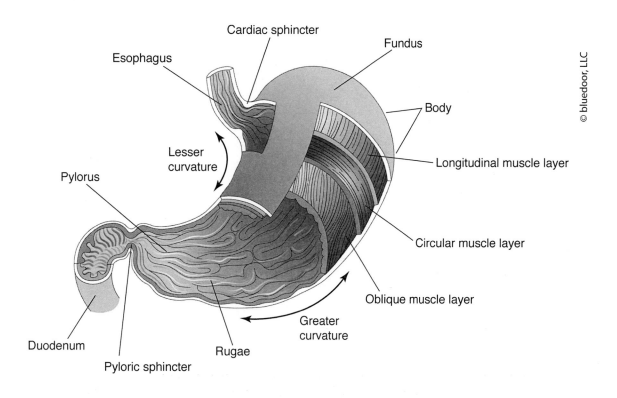

Figure 10-6. The stomach and duodenum

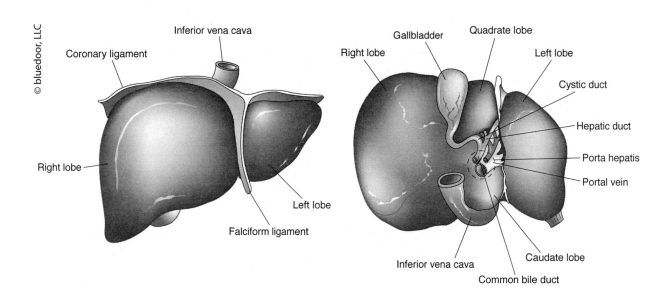

Figure 10-7. Anterior and inferior view of liver

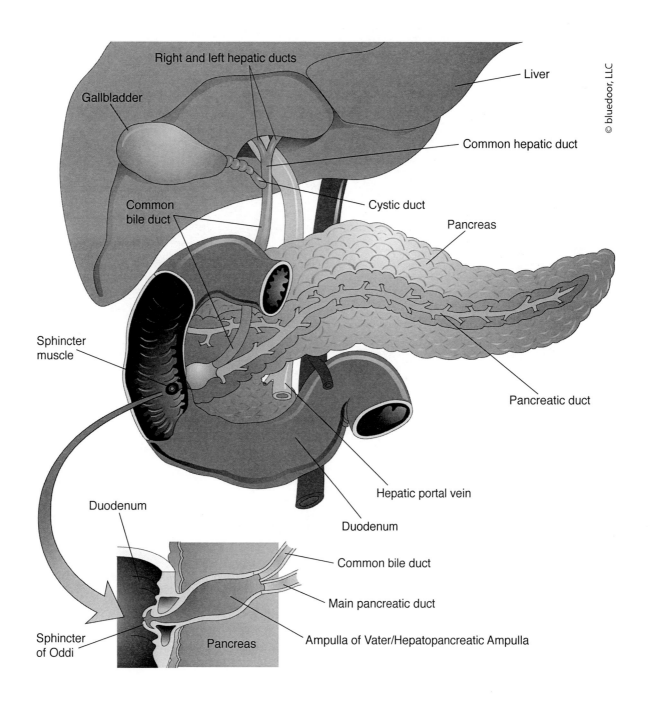

Figure 10-8. Bile ducts in relation to the liver, gallbladder, pancreas, and duodenum

DIGESTIVE SYSTEM STUDY QUESTIONS

1. In the gastrointestinal tract, the _____ _____ surrounds the submucosa and consists of two layers of smooth muscle.

2. Name the 4 lobes of the liver.

   A. _____   C. _____

   B. _____   D. _____

3. List 5 intraperitoneal and 5 retroperitoneal or secondarily retroperitoneal organs.

   <u>Intraperitoneal</u>   <u>Retroperitoneal</u>

   A. _____   A. _____

   B. _____   B. _____

   C. _____   C. _____

   D. _____   D. _____

   E. _____   E. _____

4. What type of luminal epithelium is found in both the small intestine and the colon?

5. Name 4 specialized structures or generalized features found within the stomach.

   A. _____   C. _____

   B. _____   D. _____

6. Name 4 specializations of the small intestine for absorption or protection.

   A. _____   C. _____

   B. _____   D. _____

7. TRUE or FALSE: The flexure in the colon adjoining the ascending colon and transverse colon is called the splenic flexure.

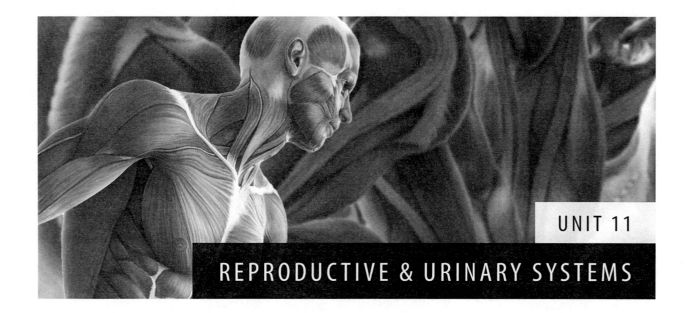

REPRODUCTIVE SYSTEM

Be able to identify the following structures on cadavers, models, and figures.

I. Male

1. Reproductive structures:
  scrotum
  testis (es)
    tunica albuginea
    tunica vaginalis
    seminiferous tubules
    rete testis
  epididymis
    head
    body
    tail
  ductus deferens (vas deferens)
    ampulla
    ejaculatory duct
  seminal vesicle
  prostate gland
  urogenital diaphragm
  bulbourethral gland (Cowper's Gland)

2. spermatic cord
  What structures are contained within the spermatic cord?

3. inguinal canal -
  superficial (external) inguinal ring
  deep inguinal ring
  inguinal ligament - lies deep to the inguinal canal

4. penis -
     corpora cavernosa (paired columns of erectile tissue)
     corpus spongiosum (a single, unpaired column)
     glans penis
     external urethral orifice
     prepuce (foreskin)
5. associated structures of male reproductive system
     pampiniform plexus
     scrotum
       cremaster muscle
       dartos muscle
     testicular artery
     testicular vein

II. Female

1. ovaries
     cortex
     medulla
     corpus luteum
2. mesenteries associated with the ovaries -
     broad ligament
     ovarian ligament
3. uterine tubes (fallopian tubes or oviducts), and its named regions -
     fimbriae
     infundibulum
     ampulla
     isthmus
4. uterus -
     fundus
     body
     cervix
5. external genitalia -
     mons pubis
     vagina
     clitoris (homologous to the penis)
     labia minora
     labia majora (homologous to the scrotum)

     external urethral orifice

URINARY SYSTEM

Urinary system - be able to identify the following structures on male & female:

A. kidney -

    supporting tissues

        renal fascia

        perirenal fat

        fibrous capsule

    renal cortex

    renal column

    renal medulla

        medullary (renal) pyramids

        renal papilla

    renal sinus

    renal minor calyx

    renal major calyx

    renal pelvis

    renal hilum

    renal artery

    renal vein

B. detailed anatomy of the kidney/nephron. About 85% of nephrons have short loops of Henle, which means most of the nephron resides in the cortex. These are called **cortical nephrons**. In contrast, the other 15% have long loops of Henle which dip deep into the medulla. These are **juxtamedullary nephrons**. Be able to identify on models or figures.

    1. vascular components of the kidney and nephron:

        segmental arteries

        lobar arteries (some resources omit these)

        interlobar arteries

        arcuate artery

        cortical radiate artery (called interlobular arteries in some resources)

        afferent arteriole

        glomerulus

        efferent arteriole

        peritubular capillaries and vasa recta

        cortical radiate vein (or interlobular veins)

        arcuate vein

        interlobar veins

    2. tubular components of the nephron:

        Bowman's capsule (Bowman's capsule + glomerulus = renal corpuscle)

        proximal convoluted tubule

        loop of Henle

        distal convoluted tubule

        collecting duct

        papillary duct

3. juxtaglomerular apparatus - a regulatory structure important in maintaining blood pressure and urine formation located where the ascending limb of the loop of Henle passes between the afferent and efferent arterioles.

granular cells - secrete renin
mesangial cells
macula densa cells

What does renin do?

C. ureters and urinary bladder

D. urethra -
   1. Male
      prostatic urethra
      membranous urethra
      spongy (penile) urethra
      external urethral orifice

   2. Female
      urethra
      external urethral orifice

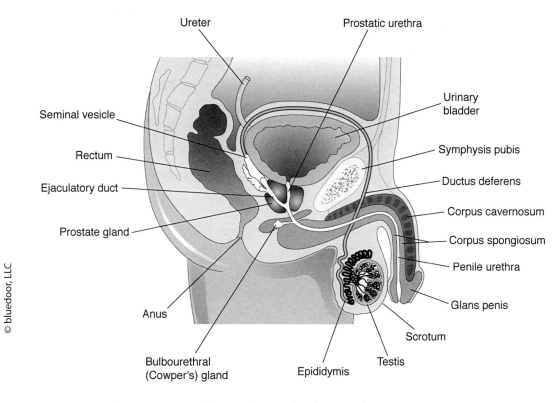

Ureter

Prostatic urethra

Urinary bladder

Seminal vesicle

Symphysis pubis

Rectum

Ductus deferens

Ejaculatory duct

Corpus cavernosum

Corpus spongiosum

Prostate gland

Penile urethra

Glans penis

Anus

Scrotum

Bulbourethral (Cowper's) gland

Testis

Epididymis

Figure 11-1. Midsagittal view of male reproductive structures

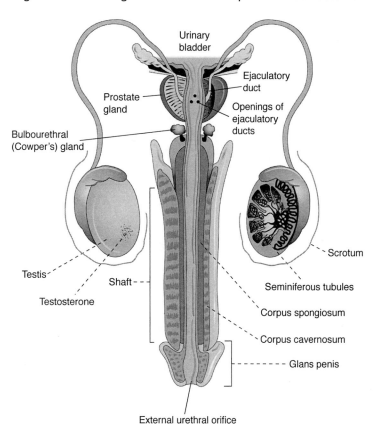

Urinary bladder

Prostate gland

Ejaculatory duct

Openings of ejaculatory ducts

Bulbourethral (Cowper's) gland

Testis

Shaft

Scrotum

Testosterone

Seminiferous tubules

Corpus spongiosum

Corpus cavernosum

Glans penis

External urethral orifice

Figure 11-2. Reproductive organs of a male

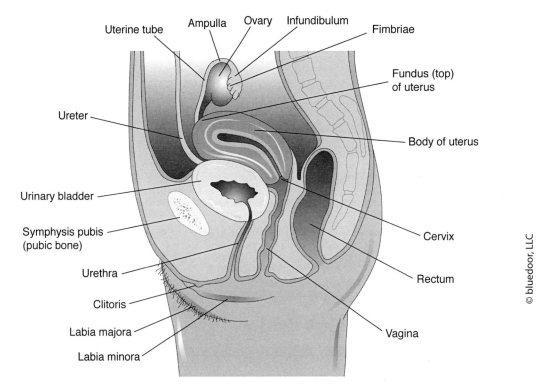

Figure 11-3. Midsagittal view of female reproductive structures

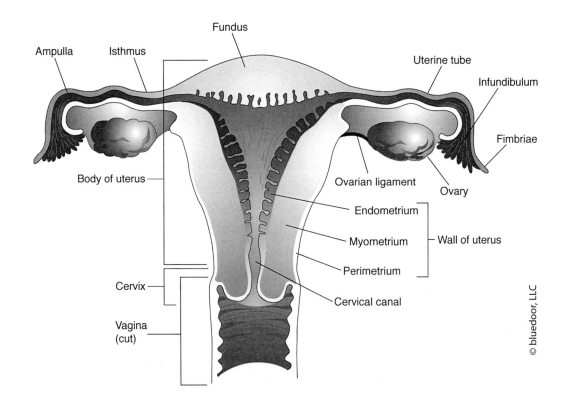

Figure 11-4. Reproductive organs of a female

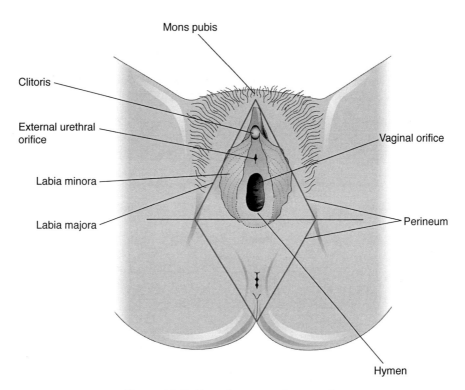

Figure 11-5. Female external genetalia

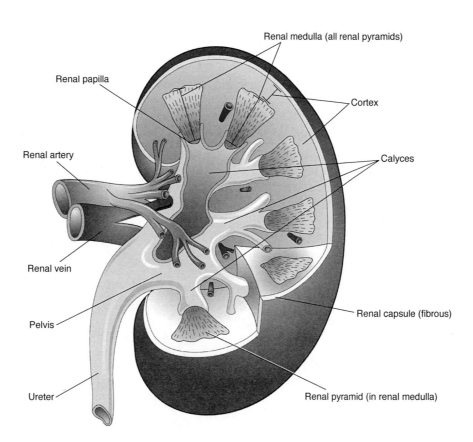

Figure 11-6. Internal structures of a kidney

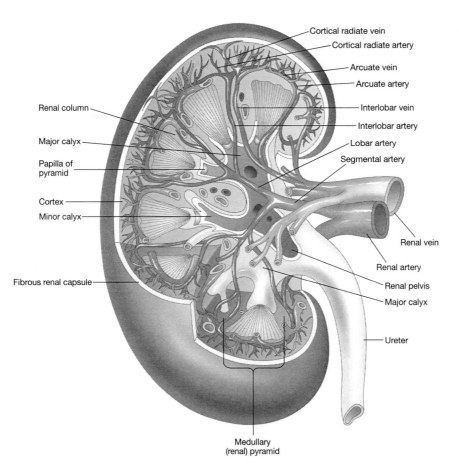

Figure 11-7. Blood supply to the nephron

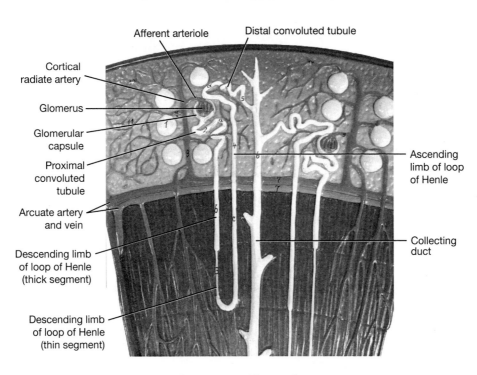

Figure 11-8. The nephron

REPRODUCTIVE AND URINARY SYSTEMS
STUDY QUESTIONS

1. Columns of renal cortex that extend between the renal pyramids are called

   _____.

2. Trace the path of blood flow from the renal artery to the renal vein.

3. Name the 3 divisions of the male urethra.

   A. _____

   B. _____

   C. _____

4. The inner, hairless folds of skin surrounding the vagina are called the _____.

5. Trace the path mature sperm travel from the testes to the external urethral orifice.

6. Trace the path of a urea molecule from Bowman's capsule to the outside of the body.

7. What male and female reproductive structures are homologous?

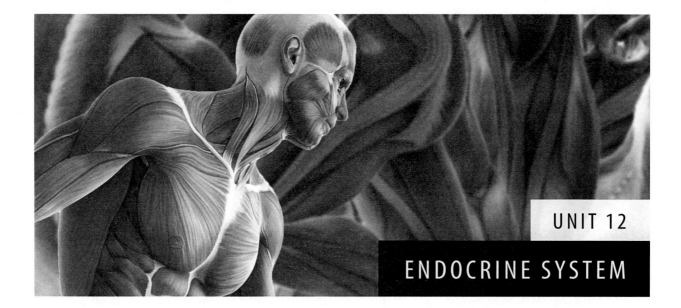

I. The endocrine system and the nervous system are the main regulating entities of the human body. While the nervous system regulates its targets (muscle and glands) via release of chemical messenger (neurotransmitter) directly on the target from axon terminals, the endocrine system releases chemical message (hormones) to the blood stream, and the absence or presence of receptors on the target determines the presence and type of response. Endocrine glands produce and secrete hormones into the bloodstream – thus they are ductless (as opposed to ducted = exocrine) glands. Three mechanisms are involved in the regulation of hormone release from endocrine glands: 1) neural, whereby direction from the nervous system regulates endocrine release (example: release of epinephrine and norepinephrine from the adrenal medulla); 2) humoral, where constituents of the blood are monitored by the endocrine gland and determine hormone release (example: release of insulin from the pancreas in response to elevated blood sugar levels); and 3) hormonal, where hormones released from other glands direct the release of hormone from the gland in question (example: release of estrogen and progesterone from the ovary in response to FSH and LH released by the anterior pituitary). Be able to identify the following structures on models, figures, and cadavers.

    A. Primary endocrine glands – be able to identify the following glands on figures, and on the cadavers when visible.

        1. Hypothalamus
        infundibulum

        Why can the hypothalamus be considered a gland?

        2. pituitary gland (hypophysis)
        adenohypophysis (anterior pituitary)
        neurohypophysis (posterior pituitary)
        3. thyroid gland

4. parathyroid glands

5. adrenal glands
   adrenal medulla
   adrenal cortex

6. pancreas
   What else does the pancreas secrete besides hormones, and what do those
   secretions do?

7. Gonads

8. Thymus

9. Pineal gland

B. Other organs with endocrine function

   1. heart – releases ANP (atrial natriuretic peptide) which helps regulate salt balance and
      thus blood pressure

   2. GI tract – various cells in the walls of the tract release gastrin, cholecystokinin, secretin,
      gastric inhibitory peptide (GIP), motilin, and glucagon-like peptide 1 to help regulate
      motility and secretion in the digestive system.

   3. placenta – human chorionic gonadotropin (hCG), estrogen and progesterone to help
      support maintenance of the uterine lining

   4. kidneys – erythropoietin (stimulates RBC production) and 1,25-dihydroxyvitaminD
      (stimulates Ca++ absorption in the gut)

   5. skin – along with kidneys, plays a role in regulating Ca++ absorption

II. You should be able to identify which hormones each gland produces, and in general the target and action of the hormone. Using your text, fill in the table below:

Gland	Hormone(s)	Target	Action
Hypothalamus			
Pituitary gland adenohypophysis neurohypophysis			
Thyroid gland			
Parathyroid glands			
Adrenal glands cortex medulla	epinephrine and norepinephrine		
Pancreas	Insulin and glucagon	Cells in the liver, adipose tissue	Affect cellular glucose uptake and gluconeo-genesis by the liver to regulate blood sugar levels
Gonads			
Thymus			
Pineal gland			
Heart			increases urinary salt loss, reduces blood volume and blood pressure
Stomach			
Kidney	releases renin (an enzyme) ⇓ angiotensinogen ⇨ angiotensin I		

ENDOCRINE SYSTEM STUDY QUESTIONS

1. What is the relationship between the hypothalamus and the anterior pituitary? Draw a picture which shows how signals pass from the hypothalamus to the anterior and posterior pituitary via different pathways.

2. Hormones from the hypothalamus travel to the anterior pituitary via the _____ _____.

3. How do hormones from the anterior pituitary get to their targets?

4. What glands do products from the anterior pituitary regulate?

5. How does the hypothalamus play a role in regulation of estrogen and progesterone release from the ovaries? How?

6. What gland releases TSH (thyroid stimulating hormone)? What could elevated TSH levels indicate?

7. Diagram the role of renin in regulating aldosterone levels. What does aldosterone do?

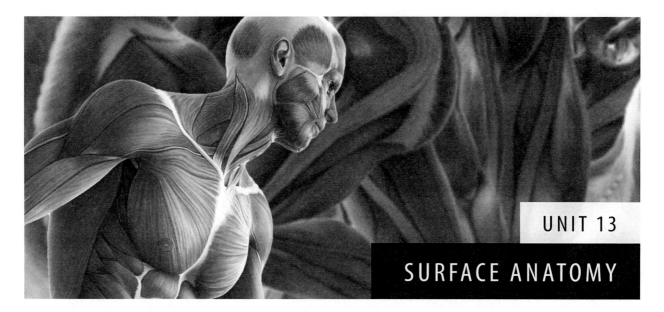

I. General Considerations

Knowledge of surface anatomy is an essential clinical tool. From rapid evaluation at the scene of an accident (taking a radial pulse) to administration of medication (intramuscular injections) health care providers from all disciplines use surface anatomy routinely. In addition, the study of surface anatomy provides a powerful review of the structures underlying the skin. The study of surface anatomy will not only provide knowledge of useful surface landmarks for identification of deeper muscles, bones, and organs, but it will reinforce the location of those structures and their relationships with other organs. For each region **identify AND PALPATE** the listed structures on yourself or your lab partner. You are responsible for being able to describe the landmarks for particular structures, identify landmarks or structures on figures or models for the practical and know the contents of regions. Use your textbook and what you've learned in this course to identify the following landmarks and structures:

II. Head Region

A. temporal region

temporalis muscle
superficial temporal artery (palpate for pulse just posterior
to the orbits and anterior to the auricle)

B. occipital region

external occipital protuberance

C. face

auricle
external acoustic meatus
mastoid process
palpebrae
external nares
buccal region
labia
philtrum (depression between nose and upper lip)

zygomatic bone
zygomatic arch
mentum (chin)

III. Neck region

    A.   anterior region

          larynx
          thyroid cartilage
          laryngeal prominence (also called thyroid prominence)
          trachea
          sternal notch

    B.   posterior region

          vertebra prominens (spinous process of C7)

    C.   lateral region

          sternocleidomastoid muscles – which divide the later neck region
              into two clinically important triangles:
          <u>anterior triangle</u> – contains cervical lymph nodes, submandibular
              gland, common carotid artery, internal jugular vein, cervical lymph
              nodes, sternohyoid, sternothyroid muscles, lateral edges of the
              larynx, thyroid gland.
          <u>posterior triangle</u> –contains the external jugular vein, accessory nerve
              brachial plexus, and lymph nodes, part of subclavian vein and artery.

IV. Thorax

clavicles
suprasternal notch
costal margins
infrasternal angle
ribs
sternum
sternal angle
breasts
nipples
areolas
heart landmarks (look at the beginning of the text chapter on the heart)
    apex - between 5th and 6th ribs inferior to the left nipple
    superior right corner - where costal cartilage of the 3rd rib articulates with the sternum. Best
        place to hear aortic semilunar valve.
    superior left corner – at the costal cartilage of the second rib, ½ inch left of the
        sternum. Best place to hear pulmonary semilunar valve.
    inferior right corner – at the costal cartilage of the 6th rib, ½ inch left of the
        sternum. Best place to hear the tricuspid/right AV valve.
    inferior left corner – 5th intercostal space at the midclavicular line. Best place to hear the
        bicuspid/left AV valve.

V. Abdominopelvic region

abdominal regions – know with CONTENTS (look at the introductory
material in the 1st chapter of the text!)

> right hypochondriac
> epigastric
> left hypochondriac
> right lumbar
> umbilical
> left lumbar
> right iliac (inguinal)
> hypogastric
> left iliac (inguinal)

abdominal quadrants – know with CONTENTS (as above)
> right upper
> left upper
> right lower
> left lower

umbilicus (navel)

linea alba

pubic bones

anterior superior iliac spine

inguinal ligament - runs from the anterior superior iliac spine to the pubic
tubercle on the pubis.

superficial inguinal ring/inguinal canal – superior to the medial portion
of the inguinal ligament.

VI. Back

vertebral spinal processes – try to identify which vertebrae, noting which are cervical,
> thoracic, and lumbar

median furrow – vertically oriented indentation along the inferior midline of the back
> where muscles attach to vertebral spinal processes

lateral border of scapula

medial border of scapula

spine of scapula

triangle of auscultation – region bordered by rhomboid major, trapezius, latissimus
> dorsi where fewer muscle layers enables clearer auscultation of respiratory sounds.

iliac crests – mark superior border of os coxae

VII. Shoulder and upper extremity

clavicle

acromion

deltoid muscle

axilla

anterior axillary fold – formed by pectoralis major

posterior axillary fold – formed by latissiumus dorsi and teres major

axillary lymph nodes

axillary artery – palpable within axilla

cephalic vein – superficial, traversing down the top of the biceps brachii

brachial artery – palpable along the medial side of the brachium, just posterior to biceps brachii

biceps brachii

cubital fossa – depression on anterior surface of elbow

median cubital vein – connects basilica and cephalic veins within the cubital fossa; common site for venipuncuture.

triceps brachii

lateral epicondyle of the humerus

olecranon of the ulna

medial epicondyle of the humerus

styloid process of radius

styloid process of the ulna

radial artery – pulse palpable between the distal tendons of the flexor carpi radialis and the brachioradialis

anatomical snuffbox – formed by the tendons of the extensor pollicis brevis, abductor pollicis long and extensor pollicis longus

tendons of extensor digitorum on posterior aspect of hand

VIII. Hip and lower extremity

gluteal fold – formed by inferior border of the gluteus maximus

natal cleft – midline indentation between right and left glutes (and you've been calling it something else all these years!!)

ischial tuberosities

gluteus medius – superolateral portion of each buttock, lateral and inferior to the iliac crest = preferred site for intramuscular injections

femoral triangle – depression inferior to inguinal ligament on anteromedial, superior surface of the thigh. Bounded by inguinal ligament, sartorious muscle and adductor longus. Femoral artery, vein and nerve travel through it, so clinically important to control lower extremity hemorrhage.

patella

lateral and medial epicondyles of the femur

lateral and medial epicondyles of the tibia

iliotibial tract or band

tibial tuberosity

popliteal fossa – back of the knee

medial malleolus of the tibia

lateral malleolus of the fibula

calcaneal tendon

posterior tibial artery – pulse palpable posteroinferior to the medial malleolus of the tibia.

dorsalis pedis artery – pulse palpable over the navicular bone or along the dorsal space between the first and second

SURFACE ANATOMY STUDY QUESTIONS

1. Where would you place a stethoscope to determine the presence or absence of mitral valve stenosis?

2. Your child has difficulty breathing and you suspect pneumonia. Where could you most easily listen for rales in the lower portions of the lungs?

3. You need to take a blood sample from a patient. Where would you attempt a venipuncture?

4. You need to give an IM (intramuscular) injection. What locations provide the best targets for needle insertion, and why?

5. our mountain biking partner takes a dive and comes up with a bad bump on the anterior aspect of the superior portion of her thorax, just lateral to her cervical region. She also has significant swelling on the lateral aspect of her leg, midway between the knee and ankle. What bones might she have broken?

ROOTS, PREFIXES, & SUFFIXES

This appendix includes lists of root words, suffixes, and prefixes that may be of use in trying to understand how many structures were named. Many of these words are Latin or Greek in origin. Many thanks to Scott Forman for preparing this appendix.

ROOTS

A

abdomin	abdomen		**andr**	male
acanth	thorny, spiny		**angi**	vessel
acetabul	vindgar cup: acetabulum (hip socket)		**anis**	unequal; dissimilar
			ankyl	crooked; stiff; bent
acou	hearing		**antr**	antrum
acr	extremities; height		**aort**	aorta
actin	ray; radius		**aponeur**	aponeurosis
aden	gland		**appendic**	appendix
adenoid	adenoids		**arche**	first; beginning
adren	adrenal gland		**arteri**	artery
adrenal	adrenal gland		**arteriol**	arteriole (small artery)
aer	air; gas		**arthr**	joint
albumin	albumin		**articul**	joint
algesi	pain		**atel**	imperfect; incomplete
alveol	alveolus		**ather**	yellowish; fatty plaque
ambly	dull; dim		**atri**	atrium
amni	amnion		**aur**	ear
amnion	amnion		**aut**	self
amyl	starch		**axill**	armpit
an	anus		**azot**	urea; nitrogen

B

bacteri	bacteria
balan	glans penis
bi	life
bil	bile
blast	developing cell
blephar	eyelid
brachi	arm
bronch	bronchus
bronchiol	bronchiole
bucc	cheek
burs	bursa (cavity)

C

caec	blind, ending blind
calc	heel, calcium
cancer, carcin	cancer
cardi	heart
carn	flesh
carp	carpals (wrist bones)
caud	tail; toward the lower part of the body
cec	cecum
celi	abdomen (abdominal cavity)
cephal	head
cereb	brain, cerebellum
cerumin	cerumen (earwax)
cervic	cervix
cheil	lip
chiasm	cross
chir	hand
chol	gall; bile
cholangi	bile duct
choledoch	common bile duct
chondr	cartilage
chord	string
chori	skin, afterbirth
chrom	color
cisterna	box; chest

clavic	clavicle (collarbone)
cleid	clavicle
clitor	small hill
cnen	shin or tibia
coccy	cuckoo; cuckoo- shaped bone
coch	land snail
coel	hollow
col	colon
coll	hill, neck
colp	vagina
commissur	point of union of two things
condyl	articulatory prominence at a joint, knuckle
coni	dust
conjunctiv	conjunctiva
corac	raven or crow
cor(e)	pupil
corne	cornea
coron	crown or something curved; heart
corp	body
cort	bark; cortex (outer layer of body organ)
cost	rib
crani	cranium (skull)
cribr	sieve
cry	cold
crypt	hidden
culd	cul-de-sac
cutane	skin
cyan	blue
cyes	pregnancy
cyst	bladder; sac
cyt	cell

D

dacry	tear, tear duct
dactyl	tooth
delt	fourth letter of Greek alphabet
derm, dermat	skin

dextr	right	**femor**	femur (upper leg bone)
diaphor	sweat	**fet**	fetus; unborn child
diaphragmat	diaphragm	**fibr**	fibrous tissue, fibers
didym	testicle	**fibul**	buckle or pin; fibula (lower leg)
digit	finger	**fimbr**	fringe
dipl	two; double	**foli**	leaf
dips	thirst	**fove**	small pit
disk	intervertebral disk	**fun**	cord or rope
diverticul	diverticulum	**fund**	bottom
dors	back (of the body)		
duoden	duodenum	**gangli (on)**	swelling or tumor; ganglion
dur	hard; dura mater	**gastr**	stomach
dynam	power or strength	**gem**	twin-born
		gen	race or kind

E

		ger (ont)	old age; aged
ech	sound	**gingiv**	gum
ectop	located away from usual place	**glen**	cavity or socket
electr	electricity, electrical activity	**glomerul**	glomerulus
embry	embryo; to be full	**gloss, glott**	tongue
emmetr	a normal meaure	**gluc**	sweetness; sugar
encephal	brain	**glut**	buttock
endocrin	endocrine	**glyc(os)**	sugar
enter	intestines	**gnath**	jaw
epididym	epididymis	**gnos**	knowledge
epiglott	epiglottis	**gon**	seed
episi	vulva	**gracil**	slender
epitheli	epithelium	**gravid**	pregnancy
erythr	red	**gyn(ec)**	woman
esophag	esophagus	**gyr**	circle or round
esthesi	sensation, sensitivity, feeling		
ethm	sieve		
eti	cause (of disease)		

H

F-G

		hem(at)	blood
faci	face	**hepa(t)**	liver
falc	sickle	**herni**	hernia
Fallopio	16th century Italian anatomist	**heter**	other
fasc	band, bandage	**hidr**	sweat
fasci	bundle	**hist**	tissue
		hom	same
		home	sameness; unchanging
		humer	humerus (upper arm bone)

hydr	water	**leuk**	white
hymen	hymen	**lig**	a band
hypn	sleep	**lingu**	tongue
hyster	uterus	**lip**	fat
		lith	stone; calculus
I-K		**lob**	lobe
		lord	bent forward
iatr	medicine; physician	**lumb**	loin
ichthy	fish	**luna**	moon
ile, ili	groin; ileum	**lymph**	lymph
immun	immune		
infundibul	funnel	**M**	
inguin	groin		
iri(d)	iris	**macr**	abnormal largeness
is	equal; same	**magnus**	great
isch	deficiency; blockage	**malleus**	hammer
ischi	hip	**mamm**	breast
		mamilla	nipple
jejun	empty	**mandibul**	mandible (lower jaw bone)
jugulum	collarbone	**mass**	chewer
		mast	breast
kal	potassium	**mastoid**	mastoid
kary	nucleus	**mater**	mother
kerat	cornea	**maxill**	maxilla (upper jaw bone)
kerat	horny tissue; hard	**meat**	passage, opening
kin	movement	**melan**	black
kinesi	movement; motion	**men**	menstruation
kyph	hump	**mening**	meninges
kytos	vessel	**menisc**	meniscus (crescent)
		ment	mind
L		**mentum**	chin
		metr	uterus
labi	lips	**mon**	one
labyrinth	labyrinth	**morph**	form; shape
lacrim	tear duct, tear	**muc**	mucus
lact	milk	**my**	muscle
lamin	lamina (thin; flat plate or layer)	**myc**	fungus
lapar	abdomen	**myel**	bone marrow; spinal cord
laryng	larynx	**myelon**	bone marrow
later	side	**myos**	muscle
lei	smooth	**myring**	eardrum
lentis	lentil		

N

narc	stupor
nas	nose
nat	birth
navicula	ship
necr	death (cells; body)
nephr	kidney
neur	nerve
noct	night
nyct(al)	night

O

occipitis	back of the head
ocul	eye
olfac	to smell
olig	scanty; few
omos	shoulder
omphal	umbilicu; navel
onc	tumor
onych	nail
oo	egg; ovum
oophor	ovary
ophthalm	eye
opt	vision
or(is)	mouth
orb	circle
orch(i/id)	testis; testicle
organ	organ
orth	straight
oste	bone
ot	ear
ov	egg
ox	oxygen

P

pachy	thick
palat	roof of the mouth
palpebra	eyelid
pancreat	pancreas
papill	nipple

par	bear; give birth to; labor
pariet	wall
parathyroid	parathyroid gland
part	bear; give birth to; labor
patella	dish or plate
path	disease
pect	chest
ped	child; foot
pelluc	clear or transparent
pelv	basin; pelvis
peron	pin or fibula
petros	stone
phac	lens of the eye
phag(ein)	eat; swallow
phak	lens of the eye
phalang	line of soldiers
phragm	fence or partition
phren	diaphragm or mind
phas	speech
phleb	vein
phot	light
phren	mind
phys	growth
physi	nature
pia	pea
plasm	plasma
pleur	side or rib
plex	interweaving network
pneum(at/on)	lung; air
pod	foot
poikil	varied; irregular
poli	gray matter
poll	thumb
polyp	polyp; small growth
pon	bridge
poster	back (of body)
prim	first
proct	rectum
pron	bending or leaning forward
prostat	prostate gland

pseud	fake; false	**scaph**	bowl or boat
psoa	the loin	**scapul**	scapula (shoulder bone)
psych	mind	**scler**	sclera
pterygos	wing or fin	**scoli**	crooked, curved
pub	pubis	**sebum**	grease or wax
puerper	childbirth	**sella**	saddle or seat
pulmon	lung	**sept**	septum
pudend	external genitals	**serra**	saw
pulmo	lung	**sial**	saliva
pupill	pupil	**sigmoid**	sigmoid
py	pus	**sinus**	sinus
pyel	renal pelvis	**somat**	body
pylor	pylorus (pyloric sphincter)	**somn**	sleep
pyr	fever; heat	**son**	sound
		sperm(at)	spermatozoan; sperm

Q-R

		sphen	wedge
quadr	four	**sphygm**	pulse
		spir	breathe; breathing
rachi	vertebra; spinal or vertebral column	**splen**	bandage
		spondyl	vertebra; spinal or vertebral column
radi	radius (lower arm bone)		
radic(ul)	nerve root	**staped**	stapes (middle ear bone)
raphe	seam or suture	**staphyl**	grapelike clusters
rect	straight	**stern**	breast or chest
ren	kidney	**steth**	chest
reticulum	network	**stomat**	mouth
retin	retina	**strept**	twisted chains
rhabd	rodshaped, striated	**stri**	to make furrows or stripes
rhin	nose	**stylos**	pillar or stalk
rhiz	nerve root	**sulcus**	furrow
rhytid	wrinkles	**synovi**	synovia; synovial membrane
ruga	fold	**system**	system

S

T

saccus	bag	**tars**	flat surface; edge of eyelid; sole of foot
sacrum	sacred		
sagitta	arrow	**tars**	tarsals (ankle bones)
salping	fallopian (uterine) tube	**tempor**	time
sarc	flesh; connective tissue	**tentus**	to stretch
sartor	tailor	**teres**	round or smooth

testis	a witness (originally an adult male)
thalamos	inner chamber
thelys	tender or delicate
therm	heat
thorac	thorax (chest)
thromb	clot
thym	thymus gland
thyreos	an oblong shield
thyr(oid)	thyroid gland
tibi	tibia (lower leg bone)
tom	cut; section
ton	tension, pressure
tonsill	tonsils
top	place
toxic	poison
trache	trachea
trachel	neck; necklike
trapez	small table
trich	hair
trochlea	pulley
tympan	drum

U-Z

uln	ulna (lower arm bone)
ungu	nail
ur	urine; urinary tract
ureter	ureter
urethr	urethra
urin	urine; urinary tract
uter	the womb
utriculus	leather bag or bottle
uvul	uvula
vagin	sheath
vagus	wandering or undecided
valv(ul)	valve
vas	vessel; duct
vast	large or immense area
ven	vein

ventricul	ventricle
verm	worm
vertebr	vertebra; spinal or vertebral column
vesic	bladder; sac
vesicul	seminal vesicles
viscer	internal organs
vitr	glass
vulv	vulva
xanth	yellow
xer	dry
xiph	sword
zyg	union or pair

PREFIXES

A

a	without or absence of
ab	from; away from
actino	ray (form)
acro	top, tip
ad	to; toward
aeneus	brassy, bronze
ala	wing
alveol	small pit
ampi, amphi	both (ways)
an	without or absence of
ana	up; again; backward
angusti	narrow
ante	before
anth	flower (of a plant)
anthro	man, human
ante	before
anti	against, opposite
apo	upon, (derived) from, (away) from
arachn	spider
arbor	tree

arch	chief, first	**chemo**	chemistry
arthr	joint	**chiro**	hand
aryten	ladle	**chole**	bile
audi	hear	**chromo**	color
aureus	golden yellow	**chrono**	time
aut	self	**chrys**	gold
		cine	motion
B		**circum**	around
		con	together
baro	weight, pressure	**contra**	against
bary/l	heavy	**copro**	dung
bene	well, good	**corp**	body
bi	two	**cosmo**	world, universe
bibli	book	**cryo**	ice, cold
bin	two	**crypto**	hidden
bio	life	**cyano**	blue
brachio	arm	**cyclo**	circle
brachy	short	**cyto**	(living) cell
brady	slow		
brevi	short	**D**	
broncho	windpipe (chest)		
bronto	thunder	**de**	from; down from; lack of
brunnescens	becoming brown	**deca**	ten
		decem	ten
C		**deci**	one-tenth
		deuter	second (order)
caco	bad	**di**	two-fold
calli	beauty	**dia**	thorough; complete
candidus	shining white	**dict**	speak (speech)
cardio	heart	**diplo**	twice
carn	flesh	**dis**	to undo; free from; negation
carto	paper	**dolicho**	long (shape)
cata	down(ward)	**dys**	difficult; labored; painful; abnormal
ceno	empty		
cent	one hundred fold		
centi	one-hundredth	**E**	
centri	center		
cephal	head	**eco**	house, habitat
cera	horn	**ecto**	outside; outer
cera(o)	wax	**ego**	"I", first person
cerebr	brain	**electro**	electric
		en, em	verb creation: in, into, through

endo	within		**hist(o)**	tissue
ennea	nine		**holo**	whole
entero	gut, intestine		**homo**	same
epi	on; upon; over		**hydro**	water
equi	equal		**hygro**	wet, moist
erythro	red		**hyo**	u-shaped
eso	inward		**hyper**	above; excessive
eu	normal; good		**hypo**	below; incomplete; deficient
ex, exo	outside; outward		**hypso**	height
extra	outside of; beyond		**hyster(o)**	womb

F

I

fill	threadlike		**icthyo**	fish
fimbri	threadlike		**icon(o)**	image
flavus	yellow		**idio**	private, own
flor	flower		**in**	in; into; not
for	away (from)		**infra**	under; below
fore	in front, before		**inter**	between
			intra	within
			iso	same, equal

G

K-L

galacto	milk		**kilo**	thousand (fold)
geo	the earth			
ger(onto)	old (person)		**laevo**	left
glaucus	bluish grey		**lanci**	lance-shaped
glosso	tongue-like		**lati**	wide, broad
glyco	sweet (taste); the presence of carbohydrates		**lepto**	slender
			leuc(o)	white
gno(to)	knowledge		**lith(o)**	stone
grandi	big		**lividus**	lead colored
			longi	long

H

			luteus	deep yellow
haem	blood		**lyc(o)**	wolf
haplo	single		**lyo**	separation
heli	screw, spiral		**lyso**	make loose, split
helio	sun			

M

hemi	half			
hepta	seven		**macro**	large, great, long
hexa	six		**mal**	bad
heter(o)	different			

matri	mother	**opthalmo**	eye
medi(o)	middle	**orni(tho)**	bird
mega	big, million	**oro**	mountain
melan	black	**ortho**	straight; correct
meso	middle	**oss**	bone
meta	among; after; beyond; change	**oste(o)**	bone
micro	small	**ovi**	egg(ovum), egg-shaped
milli	thousand(fold)	**ovi**	sheep (ovis)
mini	small	**oxy**	sharp (sense)
mono	single		
morph	shape, form		
multi	many	**P**	
myc(o)	fungus		
myel(o)	marrow (as center)	**pachy**	thick
myo	muscle	**paed**	child
myria	ten thousand	**palae(o)**	old
myx(a/o)	mucus	**palin**	again
		pan (to)	all; total
		para	beside; beyond; around
N		**parvi**	small
		path	feeling, pity, illness
necro	death	**patri**	father
neg	not, negation	**pauci**	few
neo	new	**ped**	foot
nepho(elo)	cloud(iness)	**per**	through, by means of, completely
nephro	kidney		
neuro	nerve	**peri**	surrounding (outer)
niger	black	**pharm**	medicine (poison)
non	not, negation	**pheno**	visible
noso	disease	**phil**	liking
novum	nine	**phon(o)**	sound
nulli	none	**phos, phot**	light
		phreno	mind
		phyllo	leaf
O		**physio**	nature (form)
		phyto	plant
ob, oc	in the way of; towards	**platy**	wide, broad
octo	eight	**pneumo**	lung, breath, air
odont(o)	tooth	**poly**	many; much
oen(o)	wine	**post**	after
oligo	few	**pre**	before; in front of
oo	egg	**pro**	before
ophi	snake		

proto	first		**strat**	layer (of)
pseud(o)	false		**sub**	under; below
psycho(o)	soul, mind		**super,**	over; above
pter(o)	wing		**supra**	
purpureus	purple		**sur**	over, above
pyr	fire		**sym, syn**	together; joined

Q-R

quad(r)	four(fold)
quater	four(fold)
radia/o	spoke, ray
re	back
ret	net
retro	back; behind
rheum	flow
rhin(o)	nose
rhiz(o)	root
roseus	pink, rosy
rub, rubus	red
rufus	reddish

T

tachy	fast; rapid
taut	same
taxi	arrange
techn(o)	skill
tele	distance
teleo	perfect, complete
tenui	slender, thin
tetra	four
thermo	heat
tomo	slice, cut
topo	place
toxo	arrow
trans	through; across; beyond
tri	three
trib(o)	rubbing
troph(o)	food
typ(o)	mark, stamp

S

saccha	sweet
sapro	rotten, decayed
sarco	flesh
scat	dung
schiz(o)	split, cleave
scler	hard
seism	shaking
semi	half
semin	seed
septum	seven
sesqui	one and a half
sono	sound
spect(r)(o)	appearance
sperm	seed
steg(an)o	hidden, covered
steno	contracted, narrow
stereo	solid

U-Z

ultra	beyond; excess
un	reversal, negation
uni	one
vice	in place of
violaceus	violet
virens	green
vivi	alive
xantho	yellow
xen(o)	foreign
xer(o)	dry
xylo	wood

zoo	animal	**crine**	separate; secrete
zygo	joining, two similar things	**crit**	to separate
zym(o)	ferment (yeast)	**cyte**	cell

SUFFIXES

ac	pertaining to
al	pertaining to
ar	pertaining to
ary	pertaining to
eal	pertaining to
ial	pertaining to
ic	pertaining to
ous	pertaining to

A-B

agra	excessive pain
aemia	blood
aesthesia	feeling, sense
algia	pain
apheresis	removal
ase	enzyme
asthenia	weakness
atresia	absence of a normal body opening; occlusion; closure
blast	cell

C

capnia	carbon dioxide
cele	hernia; protrusion
centesis	surgical puncture to aspirate fluid
cidal	killing
clasia	break
clasis	break
clast	break
clonus	twitch, spasm
clysis	irrigating; washing
coccus	berryshaped (a form of (pl. cocci) bacterium)

D

dactyl	toe, finger
desis	surgical fixation; fusion
drome	run; running

E

ectasis	stretching out; dilatation; expansion
ectomy	excision or surgical removal
ectopia	displacement
emesis	vomiting
emia	blood condition
enchyma	infill
er	one who
esis	condition
iasis	condition

F-G

facient	maker
ferous	bearing
folium	leaf
gen	substance or agent that produces or causes
genesis	origin; cause
genic	producing; originating; causing
gogue	leader, producer
gram	record, written; x-ray film
graph	instrument used to record
graphy	process of recording, writing; xray filming

I

ia	condition of diseased or abnormal state

iatry	physician; treatment	**orrhea**	flow; excessive discharge
ician	one who	**orrhexis**	rupture
ictal	seizure; attack	**ose**	state of disease
ism	state of	**osis**	abnormal condition
itis	inflammation	**ostomy**	creation of an artificial opening
		otomy	cut into or incision
		oxia	oxygen

L

lepsy	seizure
logy	study, discourse
logue	word(s)
lysis	loosening; dissolution; separating
lytic	destroy; reduce

P

paresis	slight paralysis
pathy	disease, feeling
penia	abnormal reduction in number
pepsia	digestion
pexy	surgical fixation; suspension
phagia	eating; swallowing
philia(y,e)	love
phobe(ia)	abnormal fear of or aversion to specific objects or things
phonia	sound or voice
phoria	feeling
phyll	leaf
phyte	plant
physis	growth
plasia	formation; a growth
plasm	growth; substance; formation
plasty	plastic or surgical repair, mold, form, make
plegia	blow, paralysis
pnea	breathing
poeiesis	formation
porosis	passage
prandial	meal
praxia	in front of; before
ptosis	dropping; sagging; prolapse
ptysis	spitting

M-N

malacia	softening
mania	madness; insane desire
megaly	enlargement
meter	instrument used to measure
metrium	womb
metry	measurement
mimetic	imitating
morph	form; shape
myce	fungus
nychia	nail
nym	name

O

odia	smell
odynia	pain
oid	resembling
ologist	one who studies and practices (specialist)
ology	study of
oma	tumor; swelling
opia	eyes, vision (condition)
opthalmi	eyes
opsy	to view
oorhagia	rapid flow of blood
orrhaphy	suturing; repairing

R-S

rrhoea	flow (unusually)
salpinx	fallopian tube

sarcoma	malignant tumor
schisis	split; fissure
sclerosis	hardening
scope	instrument used for visual examination
scopy	visual examination
scopic	visual examination
section	cut
sepsis	infection
sis	state of
spasm	sudden involuntary muscle contraction
spore	seed
stasis	control; stop
stalsis	contraction
stenosis	constriction; narrowing

T-U

taxis	turning, arrange
therapy	treatment
thorax	chest
tocia	birth; labor
tome	instrument used to cut
tomy	cut
tonus	spasm (long)
tripsy	surgical crushing
trophy	nourishment
ule	little
uria	urine; urination